"So tell me what happened," Zoe ordered.

It seemed to require a monumental amount of strength for Rafe even to talk. "I took the twins grocery shopping."

"Ah."

"I will *never* make the mistake of doing that again. I love them. But they're animals."

"Now, Rafe. Your first day was bound to be a little tough, but I think it's possible they're just normal four-year-olds."

"Maybe. But they lie. I asked them why the curtain was down. They said it was an 'awesome miracle.' I asked them why your room smelled like a perfume factory. They said a little man with green hair had come into the house and done it. And they talk, Zoe. They talk all day. They never stop talking."

"I know," she murmured. And at that exact moment, she knew something else: It was really too late to talk herself out of loving him . . .

Jeanne Grant

Jeanne Grant is a native of Michigan. Married with two children, she and her husband raise cherries and peaches on a farm near Lake Michigan. A graduate of Michigan State University, she worked as a counselor, teacher, and personnel manager before devoting her time to writing. She sold her first book to *SECOND CHANCE AT LOVE* on December 8, 1981. "I remember the date well because the next day was my birthday," she says, "and I was afraid to answer the phone for fear they'd changed their minds."

Writing involves her whole family. "The kids would probably be shocked if they had dinner on time, but they're more than willing to help me do research... from making chocolate, to mining silver, to exploring the ghost towns of northern Idaho."

Last year Jeanne won the Romance Writers of America Silver Medallion Award and the Romantic Times Award for sensual writing.

Dear Reader:

Delaney Devers chooses a charming small-town setting for the bittersweet story of an elusive boy-next-door in *Places in the Heart* (#388). Mary Alice Smith has always thought of herself as a brainy Plain Jane, and she's relied on Kip Yeager, her stunningly handsome childhood confidant, to provide moral support. But this summer, when Mary Alice returns home from graduate school, there's a perplexing shift in their chemistry. When Kip's perfect features are scarred by sudden tragedy, Mary Alice realizes their friendship is much more than skin deep. The question is how to tell Kip, whose behavior has been anything but brotherly ... Mary Alice has to use her wits, as well as her feminine wiles, to sort out this delightfully tricky situation.

In *A Dash of Spice* (#389), author Kerry Price proves the adage "opposites attract" when demure librarian Carol Tucker is unwillingly swept off her feet by larger-than-life Texan dreamboat Sam Quaide. Carol's in Las Vegas for a friend's wedding when irrepressible Sam appears and insists on teaching her the art of whispering sweet nothings to a slot machine. Darned if his method doesn't work—Carol hits the jackpot! Back home in Tucson, Carol's determined to confine their relationship to a weekend adventure, but persistent Sam lands a helicopter on the library roof, vowing to woo and win her—and when Carol declares that they can only have a fling, she soon discovers that "flinging" with Sam Quaide is a whole lot more than she bargained for!

Widely acclaimed as one of the most gifted writers of contemporary category romance, Jeanne Grant has come up with yet another winner in *Tender Loving Care* (#390). When Zoe Anderson and Rafe Kirkland become joint guardians of orphaned twin boys, they discover the true meaning of pandemonium, poignancy ... and passion. Although Zoe reluctantly agrees to Rafe's proposal that they live together, along with their four-year-old charges, she's secretly planning to bow out and leave Rafe with the boys. Knowing the painful secret of Zoe's own childlessness, Rafe's convinced that this makeshift family's exactly what Zoe needs ... even as he realizes the depth of his own soul-searing need for sweet, sexy Zoe...

In *Moonshine and Madness* (#391), Kate Gilbert's Second Chance at Love debut, Sarah Branscum, a backwoods girl who years ago fled to the big city, must return to her roots in the Ozarks when her moonshiner father skips bail. Soon Sarah herself is trying to elude her father's pursuer, devilishly handsome Allen Ames, who's temporarily filling in as a bail bondsman for *his* father. The attraction between a wary Sarah and an intrigued Allen is instant and electric, but the course of true love runs a rocky, rollicking road, as two ornery but endearing old men create unusual obstacles to the romance between their offsprings...

A classic story line takes on new meaning in Aimée Duvall's *Made for Each Other* (#392), a lighthearted romp reminiscent of the Hepburn and Tracy movie *Desk Set*. Phenomenally organized Elise Sommerfield is suddenly confronted with her ex-husband, Nathan, a brilliant but incorrigible slob, when he's hired over her head as a computer consultant. Fiercely proud of her position as chief librarian of Langley Electronics's resource center, Elise has total recall. She remembers everything, good and bad, about her tempestuous marriage, and she can't stand the thought of letting anyone—least of all Nathan—revamp her tidy systems. Togetherness is hazardous to the health of this accident-prone couple, and they survive numerous collisions in doors and restaurants—and even a carwash flood—on the way to proving nothing can keep them apart!

Samantha Quinn once again demonstrates her ability to create warm, appealing heroes and heroines in *Country Dreaming* (#393). Teddie Sullivan's a city girl who's convinced that love and career don't mix—and she's determined to get ahead ... until she spends a weekend at a friend's lakeside cabin and ends up bee-stung and blistered in the arms of the dreamiest country boy she's ever laid eyes on. At first, Brandon de Winter's lifestyle seems alarmingly low-key to dynamic Teddie, but this country boy's all man, and soon Teddie's rethinking her priorities ... and suddenly summer romance is not nearly enough!

Happy reading!

The Editors
SECOND CHANCE AT LOVE
The Berkley Publishing Group
200 Madison Avenue
New York, NY 10016

SECOND CHANCE AT LOVE

JEANNE GRANT
TENDER LOVING CARE

A
SECOND CHANCE AT LOVE
BOOK

CHAPTER ONE

"SNOOKUMS!" THIRTY-FOUR POUNDS of Oshkosh overalls hurled himself at Zoe, effectively dislodging her ribs for all time. "What'd you bring me? Where's your suitcase?"

Wishing she could protect them both from an exceedingly nasty world, Zoe Anderson simply held the recently orphaned little boy close. "I came here so fast that I didn't have time to bring you a present, but we can shop for something together, okay?" Slowly, she unwound the sticky fingers from around her neck and let Aaron slide to the floor.

"Sure. Did you bring Mommy and Daddy?"

That fast, her heart jumped in her throat. For an instant, she couldn't even speak. "No, honey." She took a breath. "So where's your brother? And your grandma?"

"Grandma's in the kitchen, and Parker's in the bathtub with Uncle Rafe. You don't want to see my brother," Aaron informed her. "You want to see me."

"I want to see both of you," Zoe said pleasantly, and gave him another quick hug.

"Grandma said she was going to have a really nice lady come to live with her here, did you know that? Are we going somewhere with you and Uncle Rafe? *Guess* what we had for dinner!"

"What?"

"Macaroni and cheese!"

"No kidding?" Feeling emotionally out of control and overwhelmed, Zoe swallowed. Belatedly noticing that the front door was letting in a cold March wind, she closed it, took off the rakish red felt hat that was one of her favorites, and started unbuttoning her coat. Her gaze skimmed the living room. She'd been here for Christmas. At Christmas, Janet and Jonathan had been alive.

Janet had been compulsively neat—now two lampshades hung crookedly; toys were strewn from wall to wall; and a TV set blared, although no one was watching it. One of the twins—undoubtedly Aaron—had recently taken a magic marker to the wall by the stairwell.

"Zoe?" Mrs. Gregor appeared in the kitchen doorway, leaning heavily on her walker. The twins' grandmother looked tired from the inside out. Her soft complexion was dangerously pale, and tears blurred her eyes when Zoe surged toward her for a hug. Loss and grief dangled between them for that moment; neither said anything.

"I'm sorry I couldn't get here yesterday," Zoe said fiercely. "I felt so bad, but I was out on the water. I never got the message until the night before, and then—"

"Zoe, I understand about your work, you know that. Just thank heavens you're here now," Mrs. Gregor said finally.

"You're all right?"

"Of course she's all right," Aaron said irritably. "She's Grandma. Now that Snookums is here, can we stay up late?"

Zoe glanced past Mrs. Gregor's shoulder. Janet's kitchen had always been spotless. Now debris littered every surface, and the counter was piled high with dishes, a measure of how impossible it was for a woman who used a walker to deal with two active four-year-olds. Despair racked her. Decisions had to be made quickly that she simply wasn't prepared to make. "Mr. Kirkland—"

"Rafe?"

"Yes, Rafe. He managed to get here yesterday?"

"Yes," Mrs. Gregor confirmed. "He spent most of the afternoon at the lawyer's, Zoe. You'll have to talk with him—he's upstairs with Parker."

"I told you that," Aaron reminded her. "Parker will wait."

Mrs. Gregor afforded her grandson one censoriously raised eyebrow. "You're still in trouble with me, young man."

"Uh-oh. What'd you do?" Zoe asked him.

"Slugged Parker." Aaron shrugged. "He deserved it."

"Aaron!"

"Come on, monster," Zoe suggested. "We'll go upstairs together, and you can show me where your brother is."

"You *know* where the bathroom is," he objected.

A piggy-back ride made Aaron willing to get out of his grandmother's hair for a few minutes. Upstairs, Zoe winced at the look of the twins' bedroom—sheets and blankets had been fashioned into a makeshift tent; clothes had been tossed every which way. Resolutely, she aimed for the sounds of splashing and laughter coming from the bathroom.

Letting Aaron down, she rapped on the door once, which earned her a bewildered stare from her godchild. The concept of privacy was about as interesting to him as spinach.

"Mrs. Gregor, there was no need for you to climb the stairs. I told you I could handle this . . ." The wet and weary man who pulled open the door abruptly stopped talking.

"Snookums!" Fast as a flash, Parker leaped naked out of the tub. Zoe dropped to her knees and braced herself just in time for the generous wet hug. Parker and Aaron both had stand-up-straight red hair and freckles and sassy blue eyes, but they had distinguishing characteristics. Parker was the sturdier twin while Aaron was the dreamer. "Gosh, you and Uncle Rafe are both here," Parker breathed delightedly. "Are we going to have fun or are we going to have fun?"

"We're going to have colds if you don't pop back in the water," she scolded teasingly. Corners, ceilings, and walls were dripping. "What is this? You've turned the bathroom into a submarine!"

A throat was quietly cleared behind her. "I had the

misguided notion that a bath was a relatively simple project."

As Parker hopped back in the tub, Zoe stood up to take a good look at the man whose leg Aaron was hanging on to for dear life. Over the last few days, she'd talked to Rafe Kirkland on the phone three times, but she had only met him once—six years ago at Janet and Jonathan's wedding. She still remembered the bold angular features, the natural assurance, the blue eyes that pounced on a woman.

Those eyes were pouncing on her now. Allowing two boys near water at the same time was an error in judgment that resulted in whoops of giggling and splashing confusion. For that moment, Zoe heard none of it. She felt Rafe's gaze intimately slide over her from head to toe, and straightened.

The pregnant silence crackling between them echoed with man-to-woman vibrations. Perhaps she should have been prepared for that? At the wedding long ago, Zoe had been a frisky twenty, more than happy to indulge in champagne and exercise her flirting skills on Jonathan's best man. She wasn't about to apologize for being a carefree twenty once upon a time, but that wasn't the image she wanted to convey to Rafe now.

Her appearance accurately reflected the capable twenty-six-year-old woman she had become. Her hair was a warm chestnut with streaks of copper; she wore it short and windswept-casual, the best style for her profession as an oceanographer. Her black sweater and white slacks accented her slim figure without being too tight—Zoe didn't own clothing she couldn't move in.

She never bothered with much makeup; her skin always had the blush of the sun, and lipstick was useless—she bit it off. Today, as usual, she'd brushed on a little mascara, conceding to vanity over her best feature —huge oval eyes that were the luminous green of the ocean on a clear day.

His eyes were definitely Paul Newman blue. She remembered that. She also remembered a man determined to follow his own rhythms on a crowded dance floor; she remembered him filling her champagne glass far too often. She remembered feeling out of her league as far as flirtation skills went, and exulting in a false sensation of danger where there really was none—at the time he was working in South America, and she never expected to see him again.

Neither the hazy memories nor the recent phone calls had prepared her for the impact of actually seeing him. He was too tall, and his shoulders were too big for a small bathroom. His jeans advertised virility and his rolled-up shirt cuffs showed off sinewed arms. He had the vitality of a man who valued the physical. The lumberjack physique was accented by a face that revealed a strong character. Sun-weathered skin stretched taut over angular bones; his eyes were sharp with intelligence and perception. No one was going to argue with that chin.

He would be a demanding lover, she mused, and immediately banished the thought. Sexy was fine. Not relevant and a little disturbing, but fine. That didn't matter . . . it couldn't.

She searched Rafe's face for what did matter—signs of flexibility in him, hints of understanding and compassion. The slash of laugh lines around his mouth promised humor, but he wasn't smiling now. She looked for any clues that would help her reach him, discovered a woman could get lost in those compelling blue eyes, and felt abruptly uneasy.

For Zoe, Rafe represented more trouble than she knew what to do with. He was a relative stranger. He was also the man who had been named to share the guardianship of the twins with her.

"This place suit you?"

Zoe shook her head. "Any place is all right by me." Ten o'clock now, and the Detroit night was pitch black. At the Gregor household, Mrs. Gregor and the twins were finally asleep. Through the confusion of the past several hours, Zoe and Rafe hadn't had a chance to exchange more than a few words, much less discuss the subject on both their minds. At the house, she'd simply taken over. So had Rafe. Neither had had any choice.

Both faces reflected strain and weariness as Rafe drove into the bar's parking lot. Both of them had wanted to get away from the house, to a place where they could talk more freely.

The flashing sign said LEEDS. Zoe only hoped the place was reasonably quiet. She opened the car door and wrapped her coat tighter around her against the biting March wind. Rafe walked at her side, both of them silent.

Inside, the bar was dark and nearly empty. Candles flickered from red jars on each table, and a ruddy-faced bartender was silently wiping glasses behind the counter. Several men played poker in a far corner; two women were drinking coffee at a small table; and a few couples were buried in booths against the wall.

Disorientation flooded Zoe. None of this was real. She didn't know this place, this man, this town. Her best friend simply couldn't be dead, not so fast, not so young. And the twins . . . there was no possible way she could take on the care and raising of two four-year-olds. She couldn't take on any children. Ever.

Rafe steered her to a corner booth. "You want a drink?"

"Maybe coffee." As Rafe strode toward the bar, she pushed her coat off her shoulders and cupped her chin in one hand, bracing her nerves for the confrontation she knew was coming.

Over the past few hours, she'd learned all kinds of things about his character that she would never have guessed. He was completely unfamiliar with kids—that was obvious from the state of the bathroom after Parker's bath. Still, with his slow, lazy baritone, Rafe had a way of soothing tempers and averting the skirmishes that the little boys were so good at starting. Patience flowed in and around him while Zoe's nerves were jangling. She'd discovered that he was capable of being in three places at once, that he did it without ever moving fast, and that nothing deterred him from a course once he'd decided what he wanted to do.

Rafe was a rock, which was very nice for anyone who wasn't disagreeing with him. It counted heavily in his favor that he was good with the boys, but Zoe hadn't noticed any of those easy smiles of his directed toward her.

Carrying a tall stein of beer and a steaming mug of coffee, he maneuvered around tables back to their booth. Pushing the coffee toward her, he eased his long body into the opposite side. She took a sip of the acid brew; he took a long draft of his beer. That ended that. "What the *hell*," he said slowly, "are we going to do?"

"I don't know."

"They had no right to do this to us."

She nodded. "I agree."

He was quiet a long time. His gaze wandered over the poker players, then the two women, but when his eyes focused back on Zoe she felt disturbingly pinned. "I spent the afternoon talking to the attorney for the estate," he said. "We're not legally obligated to make a home for the twins. Neither of us signed anything. Ethically, morally, and legally, being guardians simply means supervising the caretaking of the children."

"Yes." She understood. Unfortunately, it didn't matter. Two small children had lost both their parents and had their entire world turned upside down in less than a week. Zoe couldn't have cared less about legalities.

"One option would be to hire a woman to live full time with Mrs. Gregor and help her take care of them."

"An option," Zoe echoed, but she knew that Mrs. Gregor couldn't assume even a supervisory role for the kids. Her health was just too precarious.

"So," Rafe said slowly, "are you willing to look at any of the alternative options?"

She shook her head. "No."

She'd heard the four letter before. He clipped it out low and on an impatient breath. "Neither am I."

More silence. The bartender stopped wiping glasses long enough to lean on the bar and speak to a woman who had just walked in. The lady wore a sapphire-blue dress with a long slit in the skirt that showed her thigh when she slid onto the bar stool. Zoe wondered vaguely if they were on the wrong side of town.

Her eyes swung back to the man across from her. Every time she looked at him, she could easily picture him climbing out of a woman's bed. But she couldn't imagine him handling two volatile, energetic four-year-olds on a permanent basis.

Unfortunately he had to, because she couldn't. For a moment, Zoe concentrated on making swirls in her coffee with a plastic spoon.

She'd loved Janet like a sister . . . more than a sister. For the last few days, grief over her friend's death had alternated with anger and frustration. If Janet had asked her to be guardian for the twins, Zoe would have said no. Janet knew exactly why Zoe would never have agreed to take on any children . . . just as Zoe knew there'd been no relatives on whom Janet and Jonathan could depend.

If both she and Rafe declined the guardianship, the little ones could end up in an orphanage or foster home. The thought made Zoe ill.

She pushed back her hair, leaned her chin in her palm, and stopped fussing with her coffee. "I have a good job," she said quietly. "I could save money by moving to a smaller apartment. I'm not trying to get out of my financial responsibilities here—I wouldn't. If you take the twins, I'll foot the bill for a full-time baby-sitter, and I'll pay for their schooling. They could visit me during vacations and on holidays, and—"

He swiftly interrupted her. "There's no possible way I can take them. I told you that on the phone."

"Well, there has to be, because I can't," she said desperately.

Rafe took two long slugs of beer and leaned back. "Are we going to leave them with strangers?"

"*No.*"

"Then they'll have to live with one of us, Zoe." His

eyes seemed to burn into her face. His tone was as vibrant and low as a slow-building storm. "Look—Jonathan never mentioned this guardianship to me, any more than Janet discussed it with you. I've asked myself *why* over and over . . . but the answer is obvious: They knew exactly what they were doing. The knew *damn* well we wouldn't stash their kids in a foster home, and I don't think they felt one ounce of guilt for putting us both on this emotional hot seat. So . . . I understand why they chose us as guardians, but as far as solutions go . . ." He shook his head. "I'm in no position to raise children, dammit. I'd like to believe I'm not acting out of total selfishness, but hell . . . maybe I am."

"I wasn't accusing you of that."

He didn't want the interruption. "Finances aren't the real problem. Whatever the insurance won't cover, I can handle. But raising them—no." He dragged a hand through his hair. "I'm a seismologist; I think I told you that. My work's taken me everywhere from California to Guatemala—I'm on assignment in Montana right now, studying the relationship between avalanches and earthquakes. I work strange hours; I've never settled anywhere longer than a few years at a time. I've never even been around kids . . ."

"Rafe, neither have I," Zoe insisted. "You think I can't understand what you're talking about? My life is the ocean, my whales; I explained some of that to you over the phone. Just like your work, my job involves sporadic hours, responsibilities I can't just wriggle out of. It's not an environment that could possibly be good for young kids, and I know nothing about children."

Blue eyes snapped on green, somewhere between a

rock and a hard place. "So . . . we're in the same boat. But the kids have to be our prime consideration here."

"Oh, Lord. I agree." Her eyes were luminous with emotion. "Believe me, if it were a simple matter of changing my lifestyle, I would do it. But it's not that simple, not for me." She took a breath. "Look, Rafe, there is just no chance I would make any kind of mother."

His brows quirked up in surprise and amusement. "I could see that you didn't give a hoot about the boys," he said gravely. "Parker jumped out of the tub stark naked to hug you, and half the toys in their closet came from Snookums. *How* did you manage to earn that nickname, by the way?"

"A game called Sneak 'Em Up, which they called Snook 'Em up, which somehow deteriorated into . . . never mind." She waved her hand, dismissing the dratted nickname. "Anyway, that kind of thing is misleading."

"Oh?"

"And you're obviously fond of them, too. The other half of the toys in their closet came from Uncle Rafe, and I saw you tussling with the two of them on the bed. They adore you."

"They adore you just as much."

Standoff. Zoe stirred her coffee and then fussed with her black button earrings. When she got around to looking at Rafe again, she found a deep groove wedged between his brows. His voice brushed her nerves with wet velvet. "I apologize," he said quietly.

"For what?"

"For assuming it would automatically be easier for you to take on kids because you're a woman."

"Maybe . . . with another woman . . . that might be a natural assumption," she admitted. He just kept staring at her with that pensive frown. Silence lapped up the seconds; words wouldn't come.

"Would it be easier to talk somewhere else?" he asked finally. She'd barely nodded before he was reaching for his corduroy jacket.

The night was bleak and cold. Clumps of gray-crusted snow clung to the sidewalks March-fashion; winter wasn't quite ready to give up its hold. Cars hummed past them, tires sizzling on wet streets; street lamps illuminated a city that needed the wash of spring rains.

Zoe turned up her coat collar and jammed her hands in her pockets, vibrantly aware of the man's long stride next to her. "I can't have children," she said quietly.

"So you said. But, as I told you, I'm in the same boat."

Impatience surged through Zoe. This was so hard to talk about, and it was worse with a stranger. "I mean *physically* I can't have them. Three years ago, I had an infection that got out of hand, and following that an operation. None of which is any of your business or your problem, but I know exactly why Janet wrote me in as a guardian in case anything happened to her. She knew her kids would be my only chance to have children—only she was terribly wrong, and in the best interests of the twins, I think I have to explain all this to you. You've got to understand why you're the only one who can take them."

"Zoe . . ." Rafe stopped dead on the street. His voice was suddenly gruff and low, and somehow intimate.

She kept on walking and talking, never once look-

ing at him as she told him her story. The words came
out blithe and brisk, emotionless. Water over the
dam. No point in crying over spilled milk. All of the
clichés were operative. When catastrophe hit, life
didn't end, and neither did sunlight or laughter. She'd
had to keep that firmly in mind, because there'd been
a time when she'd carelessly assumed that children
would be part of her life. Didn't most women want
children? "But not anymore," she said, bringing her
explanation to a conclusion. "I've built a life that
doesn't include kids. I'm sure that sounds cold-
blooded and selfish—"

The presence of his hands on her shoulders forced
her to stop walking. She felt cold, smooth fingers
pushing back her hair, tugging her coat collar up
against the snapping wind.

She stared at his chin. "You know how people are
about kids. A total stranger sees a baby and goes up
and cluck-clucks and makes cooing noises. Well, I
don't cluck and I don't coo anymore; I walk on by."
She said fiercely, "It took too *damn* long for me to
accept the results of that surgery. I don't want to be
around kids, to be reminded constantly of what I'm
missing. I just want to be left alone to live my life my
own way. Maybe I *am* cold-blooded and selfish—"

"Shut up, would you, Zoe?"

He said it softly, as his thumbs brushed the mois-
ture from her cheeks. His touch was as gentle as silk,
but Zoe felt mortified. There was no excuse for allowing tears to well up in front of a relative stranger.
There was a time when she'd cried herself dry, but
that had been three years ago. Now she'd cultivated

insensitivity toward children, and she couldn't imagine where the tears came from.

His hands dropped to his sides. She set the furious walking pace, more than a match for his lithe stride. Block followed block, all in the wrong direction, but he never said a word. When he did murmur something, it was completely unexpected. "There was a man in your life, wasn't there?"

"I'm twenty-six," she said wearily. "Of course there was a man. And there's probably a woman in your life right now, affecting how or when or if you could take on the kids."

He hesitated. "Yes."

She shot him a look. "A close relationship? Does she like children?"

His sudden grin was inscrutable. "Sorry to disappoint you, Zoe, but marriage is *not* in the offing." He added wryly, "I've never been opposed to marriage or to kids, but settling down has never come into the picture, because my job takes me from here to Timbuktu in search of earthquakes. My work's only part of it, though. During what little time I've spent around those two devils, we got on fine, but that's not the same thing as being qualified to raise them as a single parent. There's no way I could tackle them alone."

They turned back, and in time she recognized the bar's lights and the all-but-empty parking lot. Huddled on the freezing car seat a few minutes later, she waited for Rafe to start the engine, and found herself studying him.

His strong profile was shadowed, the expression in his eyes hidden beneath the shelf of his brows. His

rumpled hair brushed his coat collar; she could smell
the faintest hint of citrus and sandalwood, and she
was not surprised in the least that he already had a
woman in his life. She could still feel the impression
of his thumb brushing her cheek, the strength of his
hand on her shoulder, the warmth and compassion in
his eyes when he'd listened to her.

They didn't talk again until they pulled into the
Gregor driveway. Only the porch light gleamed from
the dark house; the quiet neighborhood was asleep.
Rafe turned off the engine and pocketed the key, and
then just sat there. "Solutions aren't appearing out of
the woodwork," he mentioned dryly.

That fast, the only thing on her mind was the children. "No." She sighed. "I've done the best I can to
explain why I can't take them, but they're still Janet's
children. We've got to decide what's best for
them . . ."

"I'm not exactly in line for a potential parent of
the year award. But I'll be damned if I could live
with myself if I turned them over to someone they
didn't know."

"I know," she agreed unhappily. "Especially *now,*
Rafe. I don't think either child understands what's
happened yet. Aaron seems particularly confused.
They need someone familiar in their lives, someone
they already care about and trust, someone who had
first-hand knowledge of their lives with Janet and
Jonathan."

"So they go with one of us," Rafe murmured, and
turned to face her. His eyes glinted with a speculative
light, and his tone was thoughtful. "Or both of us."

"Pardon?"

"We don't have to come up with a permanent solution this instant, just a temporary one. You feel you can't handle the kids, and so do I, but we agree we're not about to leave them with strangers."

"Yes . . ."

"They've just had their world rocked to hell. They need two parents."

"Yes . . ." Why did she have the feeling that a slow-rolling rock was picking up momentum on its course down a darned long hill?

"I don't know how I can manage to get time off, but I will. If we took them to your place in Washington, you could keep your job, and I could watch over the boys. For a short time only, of course. But they'd have both of us there, and we'd have the chance to live with them, know them, get them through these rough first weeks without Janet and Jonathan. And in the meantime, we'd both be in a better position to make long-term decisions about what's best for them."

"Wait a minute," Zoe said desperately. And Rafe obligingly waited while she struggled for something to say. "I don't see . . . I mean, obviously we can't . . ." She took a breath. "There's no way that arrangement would work, and anyway, wherever you live has to be better for kids than where I live."

He shrugged. *"Where* we go isn't the point. Sticking together is, for the kids' sake." He climbed out of the car and then peered back in. "I can see from the look on your face what you think of the idea. You think I feel any different? But dammit, do we have any other choice?"

CHAPTER TWO

AT THREE MINUTES past six the next morning, Rafe leaned against the open doorway to Zoe's bedroom. He watched as thirty pounds climbed on her back, and then another thity pounds tried hard, giggling, to climb on top of him.

"Aren't you awake yet, Snookums? Uncle Rafe is!"

"Wonderful," she murmured groggily.

"Uncle Rafe said you'd tell us about the big jet we're going on. Come on, Snookums! We let you sleep in forever!"

"I can see that by the clock. Good heavens, what time did you wake up Uncle Rafe?" Carefully, she dislodged both of the imps.

He didn't mind that she hadn't noticed him yet. Fresh from sleep, her skin had a rosy blush, and morning sunshine tossed gold in her tangled hair. She'd slept in a man's baggy, green T-shirt, so loose at the throat that it bared almost all of one slim white shoulder. Her lazy stretch made him smile . . . and also made him conscious of every lithe curve of her body.

"So you already talked to your Uncle Rafe, did you?"

"Does Parker have to go, or is it just me?" Aaron asked hopefully.

"I'm going, too, you twirp. We're going to Uncle Rafe's house, right, Zoe?"

"First," she agreed sleepily. "First we're going to spend a few weeks at Uncle Rafe's house, and then a few weeks at my house. Doesn't that sound like fun?"

He heard the effort she made to put enthusiasm in her voice. Last night, she'd done her best to talk him out of the idea. And last night, she hadn't been as relaxed as she was now. Rolling on her stomach with her little rump in the air, she rested her chin in her hands as she talked to the urchins.

Everything about her seemed to touch him. He couldn't remember being moved by any other woman in the same way. To look at Zoe was to see a lover, a woman who spilled over with her own unique brand of feminine warmth and sensuality, an intriguing blend of fragility and strength.

They'd battled until nearly three this morning . . . a gentle battle. Children were a painful subject for Zoe— she was so sure she wanted nothing to do with them. One look at her with the kids and Rafe couldn't fathom how she could imagine herself as uncaring. From bits and pieces, he'd guessed that a man she loved had broken off with her when he'd discovered she was barren.

Maybe it was at that exact point that he'd known he wanted her with him. *Why* really made no sense. He didn't love her, didn't know her well enough to love her, but there was something there. Something haunting in her green eyes when she talked about children, something fragile that made him want to protect her, something in her smile that made him want to bask in more of those smiles. He couldn't let that something go.

She hadn't backed down until he'd agreed they'd go to Montana first. He knew why. She was sure he'd become attached to the boys when he saw them on his own turf. He was supposed to see that the kids belonged with him—she'd been perfectly honest about it.

Rafe hadn't been quite so honest with her, and figured he'd better not be. Not that he needed his life turned upside down by the advent of two children, but he'd have taken them by himself if he'd had to. Deserting the kids was no more of a possibility for him than it was for Zoe. To let her know that, though, would mean watching the fragile nightingale fly away. He'd had to make it very clear he wouldn't take them at all unless she came along, too, and that even then, he would do so unwillingly.

Maybe it was crazy to act on that first overpowering surge of attraction and compassion and simple fascination for a woman. He'd never been impulsive. He'd never acted purely on instinct. Rashness wasn't even part of his character.

At least it hadn't been until last night.

"When do we go, Zoe? Today?"

"Not quite that fast, Aaron. It'll take us a little time to arrange things."

"Do I get to take my He-Men?"

"Yup."

"Do we get to have macaroni and cheese?"

"Yup."

"Do we get to stay up until nine?"

"Nope."

"Where do we get to go after we go to your house?" Parker wanted to know.

Zoe wasn't sure what made her turn her head, but she was suddenly aware of the man in the doorway. His dark hair rumpled, Rafe was wearing jeans but nothing else. If he were any kind of normal human being, he'd have the courtesy to look as terrible as she felt after a sleepless night.

Instead, his eyes were a wide-awake blue, and his body looked all sexy and warm and compellingly touchable. The eyes, the body, and the man disturbed her. She figured as soon as he opened his mouth, his voice would disturb her, too. Rafe talked in a slow, easy drawl that could wear a woman down like erosion. That voice had worn her down last night. He'd made it seem as though the only choice they could make was to take on the kids together.

Maybe it *was* their only choice, and maybe all they'd been talking about the night before was the kids. Now, though, he was staring at her in such a different way, as if . . .

Parker anchored both of his pudgy palms on her cheeks and firmly turned her face in his direction. "You are *not* answering my question, Zoe," he said irritably.

"Pardon, honey?"

"Where are we going after your house?"

"We'll talk about that later," Rafe said from the

doorway. "First, we thought you guys might like a vacation at both our houses. Okay?"

"Sure," Aaron agreed. "Is Mommy going to be there?"

"I've told you and told you," Parker said testily. "Mommy is in *heaven*. She's with *Daddy*. I don't know why you're so stupid."

"I am *not* stupid."

Zoe leaped out of bed in time to grab Parker. Rafe took Aaron. En route to averting the slugging match, her T-shirted fanny bumped into his jeaned thigh. Both jumped. Zoe was startlingly, disastrously, sinkingly aware of the one critical drawback to all their carefully argued-out plans.

She couldn't possibly live with a man she barely knew.

Slinging one kid over his shoulder and carrying the other on his hip, Rafe called from the doorway, "Want me to make coffee, Snookums?"

"Zoe," she corrected him irritably, but he was already gone from the door.

She tried to convince herself that everything would be all right when they got to Montana. Rafe was so sure he wasn't single-parent material, so sure he couldn't handle the urchins alone. But he'd be wonderful with them; she knew he would.

And as soon as he saw that, she could get out of their lives. Away from the children, and the pain and helplessness that being around kids always brought on her. And away from a man who already disturbed her far too much.

* * *

As soon as her teeth unclenched and her stomach dropped back down from the roof of the jeep, Zoe unfastened her seat belt and turned to the boys. "Wasn't that an exciting ride?" she said heartily.

"Yeah! All those bumps." Aaron giggled. "I thought one time we were going to drop off the mountain for sure!"

So had Zoe. Her nerves still did. The last zigzag of jagged road was enough to make geographical shock sink in. Montana was supposed to be flat, wasn't it? With a few buttes and lots of cows?

Rafe's square of Montana was entirely vertical. The snow-covered slopes were a blaze of diamonds under a brilliant winter sun, and the pine woods looked weighted down under swirls and whorls of white cotton candy. A pale blue sky stretched on forever, and the air was so fresh it burned her lungs. Silence, solitude, and space stamped the area as a man's country. Rafe had told the kids they'd see elk, deer, fox, and an occasional cougar or wolf if they were lucky.

Zoe favored a different brand of luck. She liked the sea, neighbors, and the ability to drive to a grocery store without risking her life on a spine-jarring roller-coaster track that Rafe called a road. Wolves were not her personal cup of tea, and the mountains gave her vertigo.

"Wonderful place for the boys!" she murmured to Rafe. "All this terrific space, things to climb, open air..." As soon as the two boys tumbled outside, she started gathering their gear from the back seat. "I can't think of a better spot on earth for kids to grow up."

Perhaps after ninety trips, the jeep would be empty. Two suitcases had taken care of the kids' clothes, but then came the Play-Doh, books, GI Joe and He-Man action dolls, a sacred rock collection, approximately five billion unleaveable stuffed animals, Parker's blanket . . .

"What are we having for lunch, Zoe?"

"We're starving," Parker reminded her, which she wasn't likely to forget. He'd told her that at least fifteen times in the last twenty minutes.

She paused long enough to softly ruffle his hair. He could remind her another forty times about lunch, and she still wouldn't care. Anything was better than that horrible moment on the plane when he'd suddenly started crying for his mommy. Rafe had miraculously come up with a pack of watermelon-flavored bubble gum.

If she could have guaranteed Aaron would never cry again, she'd have bought a life's supply of watermelon-flavored chewing gum.

"Where are we going to sleep?"

"Where's your sled?"

"Where's the TV?"

Zoe's quick glance at Rafe was filled with wry humor. Four-year-old boys never seemed to stop talking, and they excelled in asking questions that adults had no answers for. Still, her ready smile suddenly hovered in no-man's-land. Rafe was slowly but surely tackling all the boy's questions, but his eyes were fastened on her. On her mouth. On the sweep of a blush across her cheeks. On the yellow tam perched frivolously on her head.

Rapidly, she looked away and started piling gear in her arms at the speed of sound. Next to her, Rafe did the same. Dressed in a fisherman's sweater, jeans, and boots, he looked the part of a tall, strong mountain man, and her diametric opposite in every way. She couldn't imagine why something hummed between them every time their eyes met.

She didn't like that hum. In the last few days, she hadn't had much time to brood about it though. Via long-distance calls to Washington, she had arranged for a leave of absence from her job and asked a friend to send some clothes and close up her apartment. Then there'd been all that packing to do, the legal rigmarole of Janet and Jonathan's estate to attend to, and the need to hire a woman to care for Mrs. Gregor. Sexual vibrations were something Zoe simply hadn't had time for, and she kept hoping they'd go away, like bogeymen in the daylight.

A little attraction wouldn't be nearly so upsetting if Rafe didn't keep confusing her. Ever since that long talk of theirs on the first night, she'd caught him looking at her often—a pensive frown thrown in here, an intense studying look thrown in there, a lazy crooked smile tossed in at other times. And suddenly, he was more patient with her than he was with the twins.

His patience was annoying. Both their worlds had been turned upside down because of the twins, not just hers. She'd never expected Rafe to be such a brick all the time. He'd made it darn clear from the beginning that kids couldn't possibly enhance his lifestyle, and he certainly had every right to grumble a little. Didn't the man ever feel any *anxiety?* Zoe was frantic, ever so anxious to do right by the twins. While Rafe was— well, frankly, remarkably cheerful for a man suddenly stuck with three unwanted houseguests.

And then there was that hum she felt whenever he came near her.

He'd mentioned a woman in his life; *she* should be taking care of all his *hums*. In fact, Zoe had in mind making damn sure he wasn't deprived of his lady's companionship for long just because of the urchins.

She wished desperately that she were back in Washington State, safe and sound with her three-hundred-pound breaching babies, her whales. Those she knew she could handle. But Rafe's gentle blue eyes, which kept settling on her—*those* she wasn't at all sure she could handle.

"Zoe, Montana isn't as wild as it looks," Rafe said carefully.

"Did you hear me criticizing anything?" The thing was to concentrate on the boys and their relationship with Rafe. Only a fool would imagine a hum at a time like this. She clamped her chin over a bag so she could carry one more thing.

"You like the house?"

"Love it," she said blithely.

"You might if you looked at it. Try the view to the east." His tone was dry.

"I saw, while we were driving up that road . . ." Or she would have, if her eyes hadn't been squeezed shut. While praying, Zoe always closed her eyes. Her boots crunched in the snow as she staggered with the weight of the packages she was carrying. Sun dazzling her eyes, she squinted to get her first glimpse of his tall A-frame home and then rhapsodized, "Lots of room for kids in there."

Juggling gear, she made the last of four trooping toward the door. Out of breath and feeling awkward—

darn it, this was a strange man's house—she stepped in. Where Rafe dropped his armloads, she dropped hers.

"I'll get the rest," he told her. "You relax and look around. After lunch, I'll go into town, get some groceries, and see if your clothes have arrived yet."

"Fine." She tossed him a whimsical, watch-me-cope smile. And as soon as he was back outside, she straightened and took her first look around. Over and above the twins' whoops of enthusiasm, she could see at a glance that she had her work cut out for her.

His distinctly single-man domain didn't strike her as an ideal environment for nursery-school-age boys. Not that she knew anything about that subject, but common sense was common sense. After quickly shifting the stack of mens' magazines face down on his desk, she narrowed her eyes on the wet bar. Somehow there had to be a way to lock that up? And his stereo system, too; it included at least a dozen knobs, unfortunately all bright and fascinating and at a height the little ones could reach.

Convincing herself that her curiosity was only for the children's sake, Zoe let her gaze skim the rest of the room. The living room had a cathedral ceiling with an arched wall of glass overlooking the mountains, and everywhere she looked, she saw the man's particular brand of sensuality. Rafe liked blue, comfort, and a variety of textures. A white rock fireplace begged for a roaring fire; his carpet was thick and plush and made for bare feet; and two seductively soft couches were cushioned in blue velvet corduroy.

The kitchen was paneled in oak and accented with more of that cool blue he liked. She found Brie, steaks, apples, and beer in the refrigerator. On the counter by the toaster, she discovered a lovely pair of black silk panties, which she casually stuffed in her back pocket before the twins could see them.

Her spirits promptly improved. Not that it wasn't easy to believe there really was a woman in his life, but the panties were such nice proof. He certainly couldn't be looking for another lady friend if his kitchen was already stocked with panties, so worrying about those thoughtful glances he kept shooting her was obviously unnecessary.

She found a bottle of women's cologne in the bathroom off the kitchen, another nerve soother; then she poked her head into the last two downstairs rooms. One was a laundry filled with piled-high clothes and heavily laden coat hooks. The other was a game room with a pool table all set up to play and a television with a huge screen. The kids would love it.

The upstairs wasn't as large. The first bedroom she peeked into would do for the twins, she decided, and evidently they'd already discovered it: The plain brown spreads on the twin beds had already been well trampled. Zoe wandered past the bathroom until she came to what was apparently the only other bedroom.

Rafe's room had its own balcony, a corner fireplace, and a wall of mirrored closet doors. The king-sized bed was built on a pedestal and flanked by stereo speakers. He obviously liked music. In this setting, she could already hear Ravel, and promptly felt another vague attack of nerves.

Ravel and Rafe together struck her as a dangerous combination...and life was not going to go too smoothly if there were only two bedrooms. Maybe he could sort of camp out permanently at his lady's house?

Except that Zoe needed Rafe here, if he was ever going to form a bond with the kids.

Only how, exactly, was she supposed to convince the man that he loved children when his whole lifestyle was clearly set up for nightly romps with a woman who wore black silk panties?

"Wonderful, wonderful, wonderful," she exclaimed to Rafe when she found him crouched at a low cupboard in the kitchen. The four-year-olds were perched on the counter, heels swinging.

"You like the place? Zoe, what the hell—heck are we going to give them for lunch?"

"Macaroni and cheese!"

"We can't have that until we've been to the store, guys." Rafe pushed back from the counter. "How about mushroom soup?"

"Yuck."

"Double yuck."

He nodded weakly. "You like cheese?" he asked them.

He got a matched set of shaking heads.

"French onion soup?"

"Nope. Snookums, we're *hungry*."

"Scrambled eggs?" she suggested.

"That's for *breakfast!*"

"Well, it just turned into a lunch dish," she said brightly, and gave Rafe a look that said *See how easy it is to get along with them? Aren't they adorable? Don't you just love them?* Before their banging feet drove her nuts, she lifted the boys off the counter and urged them to try out the TV in the game room.

At about the same instant they vanished, she felt

Rafe's hand sliding intimately into the back pocket of her jeans. Heat curled instantly around the curve of her hip. She turned so fast that his hand ended up on intimate territory. It took him a moment to remove it; and then, dangling from his fingers were the black silk panties.

"Now, don't be embarrassed," she said in a rush. "I just didn't think the kids should see them. I mean, you're entitled—"

"I'm not embarrassed," he interjected.

Well, *Zoe* was! She turned abruptly to the refrigerator, where nice cold air fanned her cheeks as she reached for the eggs. "Any time you want to go out for an evening, I'll stay here with the kids," she assured him.

"Nice of you to offer."

"Yes. Well, you already told me you were involved with someone . . ."

"It was never that serious a relationship, Zoe."

Her thumb bit into a shell. Sticky egg oozed over her fingers, and now she'd have to pick out the bits of shell. Where she came from, a woman didn't leave her panties around unless it was a *damned* serious relationship.

"Why don't I scramble the eggs while you make out a grocery list? I haven't any idea what to buy for two growing boys."

Neither did Zoe. "I'll cook. You write the list. Meanwhile, what are we going to give them to drink?"

"Iced tea?"

She shook her head. "Caffeine. They'll make do with water, I guess, until we can get some milk." She winced. The boys had clearly discovered the volume control on the television. "I'll take the couch," she said casually.

"No, you won't. You'll sleep in my room; I'll be comfortable enough downstairs."

She shook her head firmly. "I have no intention of putting you out of your bed." He needed his sleep. Anybody was grouchy without sleep, and being grouchy wouldn't help him form a strong emotional bond with the boys.

Suddenly looming over her shoulder, Rafe said gently, "Don't you think that's a bit much food?"

She glanced down at the frying pan. A dozen egg yolks stared back at her. Had she really cracked all the eggs? "I'm starving," she said weakly.

"Ah. For a minute there, I thought you were nervous."

"Not at all." She scrambled, fast.

He leaned back against the counter, watching her. "Because there's no need to be nervous. This whole situation's tough on both of us, and maybe you especially. We barely know each other, and neither one of us knows a darn thing about kids . . . We can just take it one thing at a time, Zoe."

"Of course we can."

He paused. "And I do understand that it's extra rough on you, feeling about children the way you do . . ."

"It's not that I dislike them. It's just—"

"I understand."

"I can't *help* it, Rafe. I know it must sound cold and uncaring to admit flat out that I can't handle being around them, but . . ." Her tone turned to a whisper. Parker was shuffling toward the doorway. He'd lost a shoe, and his lower lip was trembling.

Zoe sent the spatula flying and rushed over to him. "Sweetheart, what's wrong?"

"Where's blankie?"

"Blankie?"

"My blankie. My yellow blankie. You promised you wouldn't forget to pack it!"

"Oh, the blanket! We've got it, honey. Just a minute." She hustled into the front hall, where their gear lay in untidy piles, looking like storm-shelter debris. When she finally found the ragged blanket, she hurried back to the kitchen. Parker folded his arms around it, his grin monumentally huge. She couldn't help but drop a kiss on his forehead, and then he pattered off back to the television.

Rafe was slowly finishing her egg-scrambling project. He lifted his head, let his eyes dawdle over her face until she flushed. "As I was starting to say, I understand why you don't want to be around children. Although I really think you don't need to worry too hard that they're going to sense your 'cold and uncaring' attitude," he said gravely.

Too gravely. She stiffened. "Look, that was completely different, for heaven's sake. They've just lost their parents. Naturally, I'm going to do everything I can to make sure they feel loved! That doesn't mean—"

"Of course it doesn't, Zoe," he said smoothly, and changed the subject. "If you don't want to stay here alone with the twins, we can all go to town together."

"Unnecessary. The boys and I will get along here just fine." His leaving struck her as the next best thing to chicken soup. She needed some time to gather her addled wits in privacy. And she could make a few careful changes in his house, get the kids' gear all neatly put away, change into some other clothes, and relax away from those thoughtful blue eyes.

Four hours later, Rafe turned the knob on the front door. Behind him stood a briefcase filled with work he'd collected, a package of Zoe's clothes delivered by UPS, and six bags of groceries.

He'd barely reached for the first bag when Zoe came flying toward him from the kitchen.

"You're home!" she said jubilantly.

His eyebrows lifted as he straightened. A few hours earlier, he'd gotten the definite impression she'd been glad to see him go. Now she was looking at him as if he were a god. "What's wrong?" he asked.

"Nothing, nothing at all! I'll help you carry all that."

The hallway still looked like an obstacle course. Not that he'd expected her to do all the unpacking, but she'd certainly led him to believe that was her goal for the afternoon. "All right. Where are they?" he said patiently.

"The twins?" Zoe smiled brilliantly. "They've been little angels, Rafe. You're not going to believe how easily they're going to fit in your life; they're absolutely no trouble!"

"What did they do, Zoe?"

"Nothing. Nothing!" Carting two grocery bags, she turned into the kitchen, out of his sight. He peered into the living room to find king-sized sheets stretched between the two couches. Giggling could be heard from within the makeshift tent. "I'll unpack these," Zoe called back to him, "and start dinner."

He followed her. He'd noticed that she was usually excessively well groomed. At the moment, however, her blouse was hanging out, her hair looked as if she'd been hit by a hurricane, and her eyes shone on the glassy side of exhaustion. "I'll do that. You sit down."

"No, no, I'm fine. Everything's fine." Zoe didn't dare meet his eyes. Her nerves had something in common with limp lettuce. She'd grossly underestimated the difficulty of handling two small boys for a few hours. The twins had decided to turn on the washing machine for her. Their choice of dials had resulted in a full hour's cleanup, and mountain reception was so poor that they'd deserted the television in favor of making rubber-band sling shots, which they loaded with pellets of Play-Doh. Aaron had gotten hit in the nose. He'd bitten Parker, and they'd both cried. She'd tried hide-and-seek—didn't all kids like hide-and-seek? Except that she'd made the mistake of being the one to hide, and no one had come looking for her. By the time she'd discovered Parker poised on the mantel, prepared to risk an Incredible Hulk-type leap . . .

"What happened, Zoe?" Rafe's voice was as smooth as melted butter. For no reason at all, he was setting a glass of red wine in front of her.

She shook her head. "I don't think we should drink in front of the kids."

"I don't think seeing you sip a glass of red wine will corrupt them for the rest of their lives."

"Well . . ." She gulped it, smiled at him, and then

resumed unpacking the groceries. "Macaroni and cheese. Thank God," she murmured, and then awkwardly confessed, "I didn't get quite as much done this afternoon as I'd planned."

"No? Well, I'll tackle the unpacking after dinner. And the kids. You can just relax."

Relax? She had already failed at being any kind of positive influence on the kids. She was *not* comfortable in a man's house where she was terrified of tripping over another woman's lingerie. She had an attack of vertigo the minute she stepped outside, and the awkwardness she felt around Rafe was increasing instead of letting up.

Relax? Maybe . . . *maybe* by the next century.

CHAPTER THREE

ZOE SANK INTO bubbles up to her chin, closed her eyes, sighed . . . and immediately tensed. Something had dropped with a deafening clatter in the twins' bedroom. She heard the thundering of little feet, then Rafe's firm, quiet voice, then the sound of the boys' bedroom door closing.

Silence. Relaxing again, she tried out another blissful sigh, languidly raised a washcloth, and let the water dribble over her raised knee. Laziness felt sublimely wanton, even if she only had in mind a five-minute bath. After dinner, Rafe had insisted that she disappear and let him handle the boys for a while, but she didn't want to push that. Until he formed a really strong attachment to them, she figured she'd better shield him from discovering they weren't quite the well-behaved angels she'd led him to believe.

Still, she had absolutely nothing to do for a few minutes but watch steam rise from the blue bathtub. She liked her baths wrinkle-hot and pore-opening. Leaning back against the cool porcelain, she felt her tense muscles gradually loosen in the hot water.

Through half-shuttered eyes, she studied her body. All the parts, however distorted by water, looked basically female, basically normal. Exercise gave her skin a healthy tone and suppleness. Her breasts were firm, white, proportionate. Her stomach was flat, and when not exposed to chocolate chip cookies, her hips behaved. Her thighs were slim; she had terrific calves; and except for her big toes—both of them annoyed her—she had nice small feet.

It was a darn good body, and her pelvis was never going to have stretch marks, her breasts were never going to sag from nursing a baby, and her stomach was never going to turn into Jell-O from carrying a child.

The problem was that she wanted the stretch marks, the sag, the Jell-O.

She squeezed her eyes closed, furious with herself. After all this time, she should have gotten over it. And exactly when was she going to manage to completely forget Steven?

Being around the children had brought it all back. Aaron and Parker were the image of the kids she'd wanted to have with Steve—a mixture of scamps and innocents, love and trouble. Loving a man, she'd discovered, meant desperately wanting to bear his children. If that was basic human instinct, Zoe had learned it as basic pain.

She should have told Steve when she first met him that she couldn't have kids. She hadn't. Maybe because she'd met him at that vulnerable time right after the operation. A time when she'd desperately needed to know that she could be loved, that she was still a whole woman capable of filling a man's life. She'd loved him so much! And when she had told him, when he'd walked out of her life, she'd died inside. It wasn't Steven's fault. All the blame was hers, for not telling him earlier, for hurting him, for being less than adequate as a woman . . .

The emotional scar still hadn't healed. But she would never make the same mistake again. Falling in love meant ramming her head against the steel wall of all the natural biological urges she could no longer fulfill. And the very thought of falling in love still left that taste of acid in her mouth. Zoe, the woman, wasn't enough for Steven. It wasn't that she didn't understand, but it hurt.

An image of Rafe's face rose up in her mind and stayed there. He repeatedly insisted that he couldn't tackle the kids alone. At first, she'd understood—his lifestyle had never included kids, and the sudden responsibilities of being a single parent were overwhelming and threatening—maybe especially for a man. That was all still true, but Zoe could see how firm and caring and compassionate he was with the boys. At his age, a bachelor could have been far more selfish and self-centered. In Rafe she saw no sign of either quality.

Loving a man like that would be all too easy. Zoe didn't, of course. She barely knew him. She just wished fleetingly that he didn't think badly of her. She'd deliberately misrepresented herself as selfish and insensitive to children; she'd *had* to do that, to make sure he knew the twins would be better off with him, but . . .

Her thoughts scattered instantly when she heard the faint creak of the doorknob turning. Her head whipped around. One freckled nose was slowly sneaking through the doorway. For a moment, she couldn't identify which twin it was, but then she recognized Parker. He usually led with his tummy.

"Whatcha doing, Snookums?"

She was gathering suds together, fast . . . but not faster than Parker could close the door and edge closer to the tub. Zoe swallowed a huge lump of frantic indecision. Darn it, what was the parental thing to do? Cover herself, because he was a boy and hardly a baby at four, or act comfortable with nudity because that seemed a fairly important thing for him to learn? What about teaching the value of privacy as a personal right? But what about teaching honesty and natural behavior within a family? And did the same rules apply to a legal guardian as to a parent in this situation?

Parker overrode her indecision by leaning over the tub and studying her breasts interestedly. "Your bazooms are sure bigger than Mommy's," he said politely.

A conversation stopper if ever there was one. "Oh?"

"Mommy always let me take a bath with her."

"That's nice." At least Zoe had learned fairly fast about how Janet had been raising the twins in terms of bodies and modesty.

"Could I? Take a bath with you?" Parker sent her a disarming grin. "Mommy *always* let me."

"Well, I guess . . . if you're sure she always did? I mean . . ." Parker was already pulling off his striped shirt; he had apparently taken her agreement for granted. Zoe slid up to the faucet end of the tub, the thought of a relaxing bath fast disappearing. Saying no had never occurred to her. No matter what her feelings about children were, she would have done anything on earth to make the twins miss their parents less.

She marveled, watching Parker. It took him *hours* to put his clothes on in the morning, but he could strip them off faster than a speeding bullet. He dipped his big toe in the water and wrinkled his nose. "Why is it so hot?"

"We'll cool it down," she assured him, and immediately flicked on the cold-water tap.

She figured he'd sit on the opposite side of the tub, but he immediately arranged himself on her lap. The warm body wriggled until he was comfortable just so, and then he raised his head to grin at her upside down. "I *love* baths, Snookums," he told her.

"Me, too."

"I have a beautiful body. Did you notice?"

She smothered a laugh. "I certainly did."

"Want to play a game?"

"Sure."

The game was that he closed his eyes and she made a letter on his chest with the edge of the bar of soap. If he guessed the letter correctly, he got a kiss. If he guessed the letter wrong, he got a kiss, too. Parker liked games where he couldn't lose.

Zoe didn't hear the door opening again until Aaron stepped in. When she looked up, she saw a pair of stricken, soft eyes and sturdy legs planted belligerently. "How come *you* get to take a bath with Zoe and not me?"

"Because she asked me specially," Parker said smugly.

Zoe's jaw dropped. "Now wait a minute, Parker, I never—"

"Snookums, I thought you loved me!" Aaron's eyes immediately brimmed.

"Honey, I *do*. It was just that Parker came in here first, and I—"

"Probably she loves me more," Parker offered with a careless shrug.

"*Parker!* Aaron, listen to me . . ."

It wasn't as if she had a choice. In the end, Aaron squeezed in on her right and Parker on her left. Sardines couldn't have been packed any tighter. The best Zoe could manage was to guard her vital parts from injury and exert token control over the soap which kept flying back and forth between the boys like a rocket. A limp and sodden washcloth seemed to be draped over her head when the bathroom door opened yet again.

Strange, but this time she clearly heard the soft click of the knob over the splashing and giggling. She promptly froze.

For three and a half seconds, she couldn't see anything because of the washcloth. But then, she comforted herself, for three and a half seconds Rafe could hardly see anything either, because she was completely covered with little boys. Both circumstances changed rather fast. As she pushed off the dripping cloth, Rafe was calmly, firmly lifting one boy and then the other out of the tub.

She'd never heard his preacher-stern voice before, but she certainly heard it now. "Snookums," he said as he dried two small bodies at the same time, "is going to take a bath every single day after dinner from now on. That means that for a full half-hour she is going to be behind a closed door. Nobody bugs her when that door's closed. Nobody. Have we got that, boys?"

"What if we spill a glass of milk?" Aaron always liked to know the rules for extenuating circumstances.

"You call me."

"What if you're not there?"

"I'll be there."

"But what if you're not?"

"Then you let the milk stay spilled. Snookums is entitled to privacy. All grown-ups need privacy."

"Why?" Parker asked bewilderedly.

"Because."

"Because why?"

"Because—never mind. We'll discuss this in your bedroom." Rafe rose from his crouch and patted two bare fannies in the direction of the door. "Out. *Now.* And head straight for your pajamas."

As soon as they were gone, silence filled the steamy blue bathroom. Zoe didn't say anything, because she didn't want to draw attention to herself. Her arms and legs were all appropriately twisted up to hide everything it was possible to hide, but the water was definitely clear now. One last soap bubble was floating toward the faucets, but that was all.

She watched that lone soap bubble, and then she stared with fascination at Rafe's jeaned knees, mostly because they weren't moving. If he'd been any kind of gentleman, they *would* have been moving. Toward the door. Her gaze wandered up to his lean thighs, whisked past the bulge near his zipper, and paused momentarily on the hands on his hips. His sweater sleeves were pushed up; his chest looked massive. Just above that, her eyes paused on a long brown throat with a distinct Adam's apple. That Adam's apple was pulsing wildly. She risked only a very quick glance at his face.

She'd made a mistake, thinking that his eyes were blue. They were a brooding blue-black, like the sky at midnight and just as fathomless. Dammit, he could have smiled. Her hair had to be hanging in wet ropes around her face, and he could have relieved her unbearable tension if he'd smiled, but he didn't. He just looked at her until her throat went dry.

"I . . . um . . . they said their mother let them take a bath with her."

"And you believed that?" He shook his head, still not moving, but she saw the spark of humor in his eyes. "Know something, Zoe?"

She hoped this conversation wasn't going to be long. "What?"

"It would have been a lot easier on both of us if you'd been fat and ugly."

He closed the door behind him. And not that she'd been holding her breath, but a huge gush of air suddenly whooshed out of her lungs. Freezing, she pushed up the drain and reached for a towel. So much for relaxing baths.

Putting the twins to bed covered up all kinds of tension. After that, the atmosphere in the house plummeted directly to uneasy. Rafe didn't help when he brought blankets and a pillow from upstairs to make a bed for himself on the couch. She could have argued with him, but didn't. Arguing beds with Rafe just didn't seem wise.

By nine o'clock, she could honestly claim exhaustion, and escaped to his bed with three books about earthquakes—not because that was his field, but because the reading material in the house consisted of nothing but seismology texts and the last three issues of *Penthouse*.

Propped against his pillows in a green nightgown, she read about fault lines and snagged bedrock and trench subduction. That had her yawning. The second book had a section on how winter snowloads and increased barometric pressure could trigger earthquakes, and how even the slightest tremor could ignite an avalanche of disastrous proportions. That had her frowning. The damn fool was in a dangerous profession. Seismological projects were particularly perilous in this area of Montana. An earthquake here in 1959 had jolted some 500,000 acres.

She turned off the light at eleven, punched her pillow a few times, and settled down to worry about earthquakes and avalanches, not necessarily of the geological variety.

There was every chance, of course, that she was exaggerating the significance of this little attraction problem. People thrown together under adverse circumstances always felt some normal curiosity and interest in each other. But to acknowledge even a little tremor was to invite the most disastrous kind of emotional avalanche, with implications for the children that Zoe couldn't begin to face. The thing was, to keep things honest and above board.

The thing was, to control that hum.

The thing was, he should have hightailed it out of the

bathroom instead of looking at her with those damned blue eyes.

She was turning the pillow to the cool side for the fourth time when she heard the faintest sound coming from the boys' room. Pushing back the covers, she padded to the door and listened again. More muffled sounds. Crying?

She crossed the hall and hesitated in the boys' doorway. Aaron was in the far bed, the pillow over his head and his diminutive figure huddled in a tight ball under the covers. The muffled sobs wrenched her heart. She tiptoed closer and touched his cheek. "Aaron? Honey, are you having a nightmare?"

Two small arms grabbed for her neck and hung on like a vise. "I want Mommy. I want my *Mommy*, Zoe!"

"Oh, darling, I know..." Cradling him against her, she sat on the bed and just rocked him. In three seconds flat, she was crying as hard as he was. She didn't know what to say, what to do. His little body was hot and tense, and he was crying so hard.

She rocked him back and forth and then from side to side, and when his nose started running she grabbed a tissue from the night table and told him to blow his nose. He blew, and then started crying again. So did she. She'd never felt more inadequate in her entire life.

In time, he was shuddering more than crying, and eventually even that stopped. His body turned to dead weight in her arms, and his damp lashes lay flush on his cheeks. He'd fallen asleep. Carefully, carefully, Zoe laid him back down and tucked the covers under his chin. She was moving to tuck Parker in when she saw Rafe in the doorway.

She finished tucking and then moved toward his

shadowed form. At the door, Rafe reached out to touch her shoulder; she flinched away from his hand. Locking her arms across her chest, she stalked toward the stairs.

Rafe had been asleep until the sounds of Aaron's crying wakened him, and the lights were off downstairs. He followed Zoe, watching her grope her way to the kitchen and snap on the light. He couldn't keep his eyes off her face. Her skin was pale and her eyes emerald with anxiety. She was as tense as a coiled whip.

"There's wine in the refrigerator," he said quietly.

"The last thing I want is wine!"

"And I'll pour." He reached into the cupboard for two glasses.

She pushed back her hair in an exasperated gesture, and the words that lashed out of her tore at his heart. "Look, Rafe, you could *see*. I'm just no good at dealing with children. Already, I'm doing all the wrong things. They're good kids, dammit; it's just *me* . . . I made a mess of it this afternoon with them, I didn't now how to handle the bath, and up there with Aaron just now, I couldn't think of anything to say. He needed comfort, and I couldn't think of one single thing to say!"

All Rafe wanted was to sweep her into his arms and erase that terrible look from her eyes. "Maybe there's nothing anyone could have said, Zoe," he said quietly. "And for the rest . . . don't you think there's a small possibility that you're trying too hard?"

"How can anyone try too hard? They haven't got anybody but us. And I keep trying to tell you that they'd be better off with you than with me."

"Yes," he murmured. "Every time I turn around, you're showing me how much you don't like children. How selfish and cold-blooded you are. Come on, C.B."

He threaded the fingers of his right hand around the stems of two wineglasses and the bottle, and hooked his other arm around her neck.

She was in no mood to be gently nudged toward the back room. "Come on *what?* What are you doing?"

"It's a cinch you're not going to sleep. So we're going to try a little eight ball. Ever played pool?"

He flicked on the hanging wicker lamp over the pool table. The green felt was spotless, and the balls were all set up. Zoe wasn't interested.

"Look," she said wearily.

"The cue looks about right for your size. The chalk's over there." He poured a glass of wine and set it on the rail of the pool table in front of her, then chose a cue from the rack on the far wall and started chalking it.

She looked at Rafe as if he were insane. He pushed up his sleeves, focusing his concentration on the cue ball, all business. Sooner or later it was bound to occur to Zoe that she was standing barefoot in a frayed nightgown in the middle of the night. He hoped it wouldn't happen soon. He also hoped she didn't make any reckless moves, like flying for the door, because there wasn't a chance in hell he'd let her go back to bed alone, upset as she was.

She sighed. He took that to mean she was resigned to a game of billiards. "So you *have* played before?"

"I know how."

"Willing to play for some interesting stakes then?"

"Rafe . . ." She didn't know *what* she was willing to do at the moment. She certainly had more sense than to encourage any closeness between them, but he was also the only other adult on this emotional island with her and the twins. Returning to her bed was the wisest choice, except that if she went back to bed she would undoubtedly think. About children. About emotional avalanches. About problems she couldn't seem to solve.

She took a sip of the cool red wine and picked up the pool cue he'd chosen for her. "What are these 'interesting stakes'?"

"Not money. We'll play for total dominion—and you can break," he offered generously.

"What's 'total dominion' supposed to mean?"

"For every ball you sink, you get a minute of total dominion. A minute to ask for anything you want— within reason, of course. For instance, if you sink five balls, you win five minutes... five minutes with the kids completely off your hands whenever your choose, or five minutes in which you could order me to polish the silver or paint your toenails or... heck, I don't know. Whatever you want."

Whether she knew it or not, he held his breath while he waited for her answer. Seconds passed before he saw the unwilling spark of whimsical humor in her eyes, the first hint that she was relaxing. "Those are probably the silliest stakes I've ever heard," she announced finally.

"Yes."

"Eight ball?"

"That'll do."

"I used to play when I was a kid, but I'm awfully rusty."

"So am I," he lied. She was giving in. He breathed again, and swallowed a solid lump of guilt. Zoe didn't know what was coming, and what he had in mind was neither honorable nor fair. Another time, he'd exercise those principles.

Now he watched her lithe form lean over the table

as she concentrated on the break. She was good. Balls scattered every which way, two so close to pockets that a breath of air would have nudged them in. More important to him was watching a little color come back into her cheeks. Maybe she didn't really want to play, but she couldn't live on that razor's edge of tension forever.

"Darn," she said. "You'd think one of those would have gone in."

"They should have," he agreed, casually aiming his cue. He dropped the four ball into a corner pocket, then used a bank shot to land the six in the side. "Must be my lucky night," he mentioned.

"I'll have my chance."

"You bet you will." And while she still believed it, he plopped the two, ten, and twelve balls neatly in various pockets. Zoe was taking a sip of wine when he slowly hung up his pool cue.

She cocked her head. "It's still your turn."

"I won my five minutes," he said gently. "That was all I wanted."

"But the game isn't over. I haven't had a chance to catch up—"

"I'll give you a chance to finish this game or start a new one some other time," he promised her. "But not just now. These five minutes of total dominion are mine. Come here, Zoe."

Odd, but her legs turned to lead and her heart was strangely pounding. "Now, wait a minute . . ."

The man could cross a room faster and more quietly than a tomcat on a spring night, and he was suddenly standing in front of her. Behind her was the pool table, which had about as much give as a brick wall. "No talking," he murmured. "While you're under my dominion, I make all the rules. You agreed to those terms, remember?"

"But I never thought you meant—"

"Sssh." He took the pool cue out of her hand and laid it on the table.

"This is *not* fair," she declared mutinously. And to prove it, she remained an iceberg when he bent down to smooth his lips over hers.

He raised his head and smiled . . . and then stopped smiling. His voice was little more than a mesmerizing whisper. "For five minutes, I want you to relax. That's all. You're as tense as a kitten stranded on a limb. For five minutes, I want you to believe there's someone waiting to catch you if you fall. For five minutes, I want you to let go . . ."

His fingers threaded through her hair, and his thumb brushed the line of her jaw. She intended to move. All of this was nonsense, just a silly game. The man had no real dominion over her, no real control. She could move if she wanted to. Any time she darn well pleased.

But when his lips touched hers a second time, his mouth was warm and mobile. The smell and shape and power of him surrounded her, and that kiss just kept coming. He tasted of wine, and his mouth moved with such alluring tenderness over hers, inviting her to share a cold winter night, teasing her with temptation . . . Her breasts tightened under her nightgown, and a shock of heat warmed the private parts of her body. Still, she didn't move.

He murmured, "Your arms are just dangling there, Zoe. Put them around my neck."

"Rafe—"

"I still have four minutes left. What on earth are you afraid might happen in four short minutes?"

Well, damn the man. A kiss, she supposed, was hardly worth the effort of fighting it. And four short minutes wouldn't mean the end of the world.

She lifted her arms, and immediately felt the lance of a very different kind of kiss. His mouth took hers with devastating thoroughness. His hands possessively swept down her spine, and he molded her hard against him. Her heart was suddenly galloping inside her chest. Hunger, loneliness, the intimacy of his dark, dark eyes ... he'd have her believe she was the first woman he'd touched in years. The only woman that he wanted to touch.

It was a trick, Zoe knew. A trick of time and place that she so quickly felt like that kitten on a high, shaky limb. Her fingers clutched for a hold on his neck, but not because she didn't know better. Rafe understood too much for her sanity ... but not enough. From the moment she'd met him, she *had* felt stranded on an emotional limb ... and she was alone. No one could help her. No one would catch her if she fell.

For this moment though, she couldn't seem to move away. His soft tongue found a willing mate. She was lonely, too, and frightened—and all the emotional upheaval of the last week poured into a response she couldn't control. He had the total dominion he wanted. She was afraid ... of so much. And she had to hold on to someone.

His hand traced the shape of her breast, and her emotions became a shambles. There was something dangerous about a man who kissed so thoroughly that the earth moved. He wouldn't make a safe, easy lover. He wanted too much. He took too much.

He gave too much. His hands protected as they claimed. His lips gave warmth as they sapped the will from her. His body shielded her even as it tempted her toward danger. He made it far too easy to believe that she could fill his world, banish the loneliness, and when he finally lifted his head, she still wanted to believe. His eyes were a searing blue, luminous with need. The way he looked at her was more intimate, more knowing, more possessive than even his touch had been. "You're beautiful," he said softly.

She shook her head.

"Yes." He stroked her hair. "I knew you'd be fire. And sweetness. I didn't know how much. Lord, you're so giving."

"I'm not," she breathed. When he said nothing, she stepped back from him. "Rafe, this can't happen again."

She wanted an answer, but got none. He made no move to stop her from leaving the room, but she could feel his eyes on her back until she was out of his sight. A shiver chased up her spine as she climbed the stairs.

Long after the household was totally still, she lay wide awake in the darkness.

CHAPTER FOUR

AT 5:45 THE next morning, coffee was perking and so was Zoe. Wearing a favorite striped shirt tucked neatly into jeans, she'd already set the table for four and was dipping bread into egg batter for French toast. Although she suspected that no sane human being would choose to be awake at this ungodly hour, she felt ready for anything.

Her whole problem the night before, she'd told herself, was exhaustion. When she was overtired, a woman would be prone to exaggerate things . . . like magic, for example. Like the impact of an embrace. Like the empathy and caring that had miraculously seemed to spring up between two relative strangers.

At two o'clock in the morning, she'd still been reading herself the riot act. Rafe already had a woman, and

55

Zoe was smart enough to understand the dangerous relationship of chemistry, convenience, and forced proximity. More important than that, she seemed to have totally forgotten the only reason she was here, which was to ease the kids into Rafe's life. She wasn't about to forget that again. No more kisses. No more total-dominion games. No more hums.

"Good morning!" She greeted the pair of mop-haired redheads in the door.

Parker was trailing his blanket; Aaron was just behind him. Both had managed to put on overalls and shirts, but they had shared socks. Each wore a blue and a red one.

"What's for breakfast, Snookums?" Parker asked.

"French toast. Sound good?"

Aaron squinched his nose. "I hate French toast."

"Ah . . ." Without the least hesitation, Zoe scooped the French toast off the sizzling griddle and plopped it into the disposal. "Scrambled eggs, then." She added several more eggs to what had been the beginnings of French-toast batter and congratulated herself on being flexible. Nothing could throw her if she didn't let it, another principle she seemed to have forgotten yesterday.

"Where's Uncle Rafe?"

"Still sleeping. We'll be real quiet until he wakes up, okay?" She shot a quick look at Aaron. His cheeks were a healthy pink and his eyes bright. There was no sign of his tears from the night before.

"What're we going to do today?"

"Well . . ." A good question. "Uncle Rafe is going to work. And we're going to"—she hesitated—"build a snowman and maybe bake cookies?" She poured two small glasses of orange juice and set them carefully on opposite ends of the table. She was learning: Large glasses made large spills, and only a masochist would allow the two boys to sit next to each other.

The twins were halfway through their eggs and Zoe was gulping coffee when she heard a knock on the back door.

"Anybody home?"

Before Zoe could answer, a woman was stomping the snow off her boots in the laundry room and wandering through to the kitchen. "Hi there. You must be Zoe. And these are the twins?"

Zoe swallowed a mouthful of coffee fast. The blonde was tall and perhaps in her early thirties. Beneath a down jacket, a mauve cashmere sweater and navy slacks accented a lush figure. Her hair was a long swath of pure honey, and her eyes were a clear dark brown with lashes a normal woman would have killed for.

Offhand, the only thing Zoe wasn't prepared for this early in the morning was a meeting with the owner of the black silk panties. In the meantime, the woman was smiling at her, friendly fashion. And in another meantime, the twins seemed to have completely disappeared —or at least slid instantly off their chairs and hidden under the kitchen table at the first sign of a stranger. "Come on out of there," Zoe hissed at the twins, and smiled at the blonde. "Yes, I'm Zoe Anderson. And you're . . . ?"

"Sarah Robertson. A friend of Rafe's. I brought over a sled for the kids."

Both kids' heads popped up from under the table, but neither ventured any farther. "That was nice of you," Zoe said cheerfully, and motioned them up with frantic hand movements behind her back. "Can I get you a cup of coffee?"

"Sure. Rafe up yet?" Sarah settled easily in a chair at the table as if she belonged there.

"Not quite."

"I figured you'd all be here by yesterday, but I never had a chance to call. I work with Rafe," she explained. "And I don't live all that far from here, so I kept an eye on the place while he was gone. He didn't tell me all the details, but I have a little idea what you two have had to take on." She shook her head sympathetically. "You could have knocked me over with a feather when he called from Detroit and said he was coming back with . . ." She cast a tactful eye toward the twins.

"Yes." Zoe set a mug in front of her.

"If there's anything I can do to help, let me know. I come from a family of nine, so I've been around kids all my life." She bent down to peek under the table. "Hi, boys," she said casually, and then straightened, winking at Zoe. "I brought them something else. There are two packages wrapped in yellow sitting on the washing machine. For when they get around to deciding I'm not such a terrifying stranger."

The twins decided that in three seconds flat. While with blissful grins they unwrapped their shiny new Gobots, Zoe analyzed everything about Rafe's lady that she could conceivably analyze in the space of a few minutes.

Sarah wasn't exactly a beauty, but her smile was darn near breathtaking, and her voice had vibrations that Zoe figured a man would pant for. That Rafe would pant for. She radiated an easy confidence; Zoe figured Rafe would like that, too.

Zoe searched harder for a fault, and found only maturity, a subtle sense of humor, and a warmth that was completely natural. On top of that, Sarah obviously liked kids—and the kids were warming up to her as though they'd just discovered candy.

She was a little top heavy, but altogether, if Zoe had had nothing to do all day but pick out a woman who might suit Rafe, Sarah was it. Intellectually, she was pleased that he showed such good taste in women. And Zoe was well aware that a building relationship between Sarah and Rafe could solve the problem of the twins in very short order.

But emotionally, the woman grated on her nerves.

"I know this was early for a visit, but I figured Rafe would be heading to work around eight. If I picked him up, I thought that might leave you the jeep if you needed it. You must be feeling pretty stranded out here in the middle of nowhere."

"Actually, I absolutely love it here. Would you like some breakfast?" Zoe asked politely. Sarah was a marvel of consideration. She also certainly knew all kinds of things about Rafe's private life, and was tactfully making sure Zoe understood she didn't care that another woman was living in Rafe's house.

Hell's bells, Zoe thought irritably. I'm not exactly pock-faced. And if those were my black panties, lady, you can bet your boots I'd have something to say about another woman roaming around in his life, and never mind all the extenuating circumstances.

"Well, good morning, sleepyhead!" Sarah said teasingly. Her instant smile could have lit up a sky, and all because a certain man was standing in the doorway.

Zoe lanced a searing look at that smile before her head whipped toward Rafe.

"I heard voices in here, but I thought it was just Zoe and the kids." Rafe's gaze slid from Sarah to Zoe and stayed there. Last night, she'd been as warm and responsive as any woman he'd ever met. This morning, her body was rigid with tension, she was moving at the speed of light around the kitchen, and her smile could have frozen the Amazon River.

He swung the boys up for a good-morning hug and listened to Sarah's easy chatter, never taking his eyes off Zoe. The lady more than fascinated him. Life had handed her such a blow, and maybe he'd initially been affected by a blend of chemistry and compassion. Unfortunately, hour by hour, his feelings were growing into more than that.

Caring about her could only complicate their predicament. He knew that, but advising himself to keep things merely friendly was about as effective as cautioning iron filings not to gather around a magnet. He wanted to know about that man in her past; he wanted to know how on earth she'd managed to delude herself into believing she was selfish. He wanted to hold her. Touch, claim, comfort, understand.

From the crisp way she slammed his coffee mug on the counter, he figured she'd be happier if he took off for the North Pole.

". . . so I thought you'd probably leave the jeep here and I'd just drive you in. No problem if that doesn't suit you, Rafe, I just thought I'd offer . . ."

Rafe swung his gaze back to Sarah. "Fine, I appreciate it," he agreed thoughtfully.

Both boys got a good-bye hug. Zoe got a list of

phone numbers, the keys to the jeep, and instructions on how to get to town. Sarah considerately added her work phone number in case Zoe couldn't reach Rafe in an emergency, adding that her family lived in the area and would be glad to help out if Zoe got in a pinch. He still hadn't gotten her to look at him.

Fifteen minutes later, Rafe and Sarah headed for her truck. He climbed into the driver's seat, and Sarah handed him the keys. She said something to him; he didn't hear. His gaze was peeled on Zoe's face at the kitchen window.

"Just a minute," he murmured to Sarah, and stalked back toward the house with his hands jammed in his pockets.

She didn't even look up when he walked in. Her head was lowered in total concentration on the soapsuds in the sink.

"Are you the kind of woman to jump to conclusions, Zoe?" he asked casually.

She shot him her best bewildered frown. "I can't imagine what you're talking about."

"No? Well, we'll discuss it later."

"There's absolutely nothing to discuss," she started to say, but the back door had already closed with a snap.

Busily mixing cookie batter, Zoe glanced at the clock on the kitchen wall. Three minutes past three. Exactly three minutes had passed since the last time she'd looked. Her back, neck, knees, hands, and nerves felt as if she'd been through a war. This had to be the longest day she could ever remember.

Every task had taken ages to accomplish. She'd spent an hour making a snowman, and approximately five hours getting the kids in and out of their snowsuits. At home, she could have tossed in a wash and made a few beds in minutes; those simple projects had stretched to an hour because of little-boy-type interruptions. Four games of go fish had lasted forever. She'd pushed Skeletor around in a mock battle with He-Man on the living room rug for at least a lifetime, but of course all of that was an exaggeration. She knew darn well she'd never been out of the kitchen for more than four minutes between drinks, spills, lunches, cocoa, and cookie baking.

She glanced at the clock again. Four minutes past three. Rafe wouldn't be home for another two hours. She certainly didn't want him home; she wanted him busy at work building a serious relationship with Sarah, but she felt so . . . stranded.

Was it normal for two four-year-old boys to try to kill each other every fifteen minutes? What was the appropriate thing to say when one discovered them practicing their aim from three feet away from the toilet? Had Janet *really* let them eat their lunch upside down? How much cookie batter could she remember her mother letting her lick without risking her getting sick?

She'd die if the kids got sick.

"How's *that* look, Zoe?"

She glanced at the cookie sheet. Some of the blobs of batter would have filled a teaspoon; others would have filled half a cup. "Wonderful," she said.

"What are we going to do after this, Snookums?"

Die. Nap. "I could read you a story," she suggested.

Reading a story, she discovered, was a ritual. Thumbs went in mouths; each boy glued himself to one side of her; and since she had to put her arms around both of them, the boys took turns holding the book.

Interruptions like oven buzzers for burned cookies were followed by a vigorous resettling in the same spot on the couch. They were so quiet that she vaguely worried that they'd both gone into a catatonic state, but that posed yet another question to ask Rafe. Where was the nearest children's bookstore?

At four forty-five, the kids seemed reasonably settled in front of the television, and Zoe slipped into the bathroom to wash her face. Her appearance in the mirror appalled her. She not only felt as if she'd been through a war, she looked it. Hastily, she washed, tucked, brushed, and was just reaching for her mascara wand and lipstick when both boys showed at the door.

"Whatcha doing, Snookums?" Parker demanded.

"I thought you liked that cartoon . . ."

"The screen's all wavy. What's that?"

"Mascara." Zoe carefully removed a lipstick tube from Aaron's hand.

"What's it for?"

Alarmed, she saw Aaron was ready to cry. "To make your eyes look bigger," she said distractedly to Parker.

"What's wrong with your eyes the way they are?"

"*Why* can't I put some on?" Aaron demanded. "Mommy let me put hers on."

"Look, you can spray perfume on me, okay?" Zoe said desperately to Aaron.

"What's perfume have to do with eyes?" Parker looked irritated. "Look, numbskull, I'm trying to talk to Snookums."

"Oh, shut up, Parker. What's this?" Aaron had discovered her cosmetics bag, and he wasn't content until he'd seen for himself exactly what every item was.

As a result, Zoe was made up for a formal ball when

Rafe walked in the door, and all three of them were wearing perfume and sporting powdered noses.

His nostrils flared slightly when both boys ran to him with a whoop of a hello. Zoe flushed clear to her toes and headed for the kitchen. Cookie pans sat on the counter; she'd forgotten them. She'd meant to have everything cleaned up by the time Rafe arrived. She'd also meant to have dinner started.

Rafe followed her in, toting the twins. Hurriedly rinsing dishes and wiping off the counters, Zoe heard an embarrassing stream of conversation about her eyes, which needed black stuff, her lopsided snowman, and her inability to win at go fish.

On top of that, her heart started thumping the minute he walked in the door and hadn't stopped since. She was only glad to see him because of the boys, of course. Except that when those blue eyes pounced on her, she was inclined to completely forget the boys and Sarah and remember nothing but the night before . . . how intimately he'd held her, how strong and warm his embrace had been, how comfortable and natural it had felt to turn to him.

"Nope, we're not having macaroni and cheese again," Rafe told Parker. "We're taking Zoe out to dinner."

No wonder her knees went weak. Not that Zoe wanted to be put to the test, but there was a good chance she'd have sold her soul to the devil rather than wash any more dishes. "You think we can manage them? I mean, out in public?" She felt she had to voice a token objection.

"Of course we can. You boys go wash your faces." Zoe headed for the door with the troops, but Rafe grabbed her hand. "Not you," he said gravely. "You look fine. In fact, you look incredibly good."

The compliment startled her, but not for long. "You don't understand. No rational person would leave them alone in a bathroom together."

"Nonsense." His thumb dawdled on her wrist, tracing the delicate veins, quickening her pulse.

She glanced down to see her palm lying in his, limply accepting a touch that was dangerously close to a caress, inviting more. Had a few hours with a couple of small kids really made her feel that desperate for contact? *Hand, would you move? Please?* "How was work?" She had to find something to say.

"I was surrounded by magnetometers and scintillation counters. Now how did you survive today?"

"Fine."

"No, you didn't. How bad was it?" When she opened her mouth to deny any problem, he shook his head. "Look, there's no reason to lie, not with me. I already know how you feel about kids, but it isn't just that. You think I can't appreciate how hard your day has been? I don't know any more about parenting than you do, and I think I made it pretty clear that there's no way in hell kids could fit in my lifestyle. Kiddo, if you can complain to anyone, it's me."

"Rafe, I don't think it would be as impossible as you think to have them fit into your life—"

"The only reason it's working at all is because you're here," he said firmly. He knew that if she thought for a minute he could cope with the boys alone, she'd run away. With deliberate emphasis, he continued, "If I'd wanted kids, Zoe, I would have taken on the responsibility long before this."

That wasn't what she wanted to hear. She'd hoped so much that his feelings were at least starting to change. "You know, they behave like angels for *you*."

"Yeah. Because I'm six feet three. Only one of these days, the little devils are going to discover that I'm scared witless of them."

He made her smile. In fact, he made her smile all through dinner. He never even blinked when a french fry went flying through the air or when Parker let out a burp that sent both boys into fits of giggles. He answered what seemed like four thousand questions beginning with the word *why,* wiped up a spill, and escorted each little boy to the mens' room at least nine hundred times.

With Zoe, he barely exchanged five words. Who could talk? Zoe hadn't been in a family restaurant in a long time. Mothers were wolfing down their food in the vague hope they'd finish before the kids got antsy. Fathers were radiating patience. The route to the bathrooms needed a traffic light. The noise level rivaled that of a baseball stadium on opening day.

"You've been here before?" she questioned Rafe.

He shook his head with a wry grin. "Never. But I figured it had to be reasonably safe to come here from their ads in the paper."

The place *was* safe, the man less so. Rafe kept drawing her eyes to him . . . for his quietness and patience, the way he took charge, the way his mouth twisted in a smile. He repeatedly claimed he didn't want the responsibility of children, yet nothing threw him where the kids were concerned.

Where *she* was concerned seemed to be the problem. He had a way of looking at her that made her feel drenched in softness, as though she was special to him, as though in the middle of chaos they were surrounded by an intimate privacy that just had to do with two people.

It was dark when they drove home, and few lights marked the road once they left the small Montana town of Logansville. Under the cover of darkness, Zoe stole pensive glances at Rafe's shadowed profile. He wasn't an easy man to understand, and she had to remind herself to be careful. She was alone, far away from her life and job, tossed into an emotional whirlpool because of the children. It would be far too easy to turn to Rafe out of need, but involvement would impossibly complicate both their lives, and perhaps prove detrimental to the twins.

When they arrived home, the kids suggested a bargain: They would promise total peace and quiet if they were allowed to watch television for a half-hour. Rafe agreed, and steered Zoe into the kitchen, where he put water on for coffee—decaf and instant at that hour.

"They'll never let us drink an entire cup in peace," Zoe warned him wryly.

Rafe took the tinfoil off the huge pan of chocolate-chip cookies and then offered the tray to her.

"They're all for you," she said politely.

"Thanks."

"If they help me with any more cooking projects, we may all starve."

"I can see that." He leaned back against the counter and nibbled on one. "They're not that bad."

"What'd you get—a tiny burned one or one of those huge ones that still look like unbaked batter?" The kettle was boiling. Zoe lifted it off the burner, turned off the heat, and reached for cups.

Rafe figured that was enough casual chatter. Maybe she'd forgotten that she'd treated him like yesterday's newspaper that morning, but he hadn't. "Those were Sarah's black panties you found in the kitchen . . . but I think you already guessed that, didn't you?"

The damn kettle spat a drop of boiling water on her finger. She shook her hand and then started pouring. "Forget it, Rafe."

He wasn't about to let it go. "I've known her for two years, ever since I moved here. I got to know her because I work with her. Her husband left her about a year ago."

"Which is none of my business," Zoe said firmly.

Rafe was blunt and his tone quiet. "Our relationship is simply a friendship—but, yes, I've slept with her several times. She was lonely as hell, and her ex-husband was a bastard. If you want it clear as glass, she'd occasionally come over here when she wanted a man." Honesty vibrated in his voice. "I don't want you to think badly of her, Zoe. She's a good lady."

"A *wonderful* lady," Zoe agreed instantly.

"But not for me. It was never any more than a casual relationship. She knew that, and so did I. There was a time when we could fill a few needs for each other, and that's all it amounted to." He added, "I talked to her this morning."

What he talked to her about Zoe didn't want to know. She also didn't want the mug of coffee in her hands, or to be alone in a softly lit kitchen with him. She set the mug down. The whole problem with being close to Rafe . . . was being close to Rafe.

She said nothing for a moment, because she couldn't think of a thing to say, and then a crash interrupted that silence—a glass-splintering, explosion-type crash. The lights went out.

She collided with Rafe on the rush for the door.

CHAPTER FIVE

As soon as Zoe reached the living room, she was surrounded by darkness and two frantic boys. An acrid odor of smoke permeated the room. "Good Lord! What were you two doing!"

She couldn't tell one voice from another in the pitch-black room, and they were both talking at once. "The lamp just fell all to pieces; I didn't mean to—"

"What'd you expect to happen when you threw the book at it, stupid?"

Rafe clamped a hand on her shoulder from behind. "Keep them away from it, Zoe. I'll unplug the lamp and change the fuse."

Grabbing the little ones, she tried to soothe and calm and at the same time determine just how the disaster had happened. Both boys were safely stashed on the couch next to her when the lights snapped on again, and then her eyes widened in shock at the wreckage. Rafe's huge porcelain lamp was in shards on the floor, its shade bent grotesquely. A leatherbound textbook lay in the center of the mess.

"All right. Who threw the book?" Rafe hadn't taken long to return from the fuse box. Standing in the doorway, he looked like ten feet of cold male fury.

Total silence, then "me." Zoe stood up, but Aaron wrapped his arms around her hips in a viselike grasp.

"You know what's going to happen to you, don't you?" Rafe said sternly.

"Yup," Aaron said sadly.

"And right now."

"Yup," the little boy agreed again.

"Now, wait a minute," Zoe said frantically. "Rafe, I'm sure it was an acci—"

"Aaron, upstairs," Rafe ordered.

"Yup." Aaron quietly pried his fingers away from Zoe's hip. Her arm tightened protectively around his shoulders.

"You haven't even heard what happened!" she yelled at Rafe.

His voice was as calm and cold as the ocean in November. "I don't need to hear a darn thing. I can see the book. He admitted he threw it. Upstairs, Aaron."

"Yup." Resigned to his fate, Aaron lowered his head, ducked out from under Zoe's hold, and headed for the stairs. He climbed them as heavily as if he were old and weary.

Zoe rushed after him, but Rafe reached the landing first.

"Stay out of it," he said quietly.

"I won't. Darn it, you can't mean this! You're angry, Rafe. You can't deal with him when you're this mad—"

"I sure as hell can."

"It was an *accident!*"

"It was deliberate. And he knows it."

"He's only four years old!" They were at the door to the twins' bedroom. Startled, Zoe noted Aaron had already bent over the bed, bottom up. One might almost think he'd been through this before. She flashed a look at the child, and then at Rafe.

His eyes were blue-black, and his jaw like iron. He was too big a man, too powerful, too strong . . . and all that patience he'd been famous for was gone. Rafe was flat-out furious.

With some vague thought of protecting Aaron, she hurled herself over him. Firm hands settled around her waist and lifted her off the small trembling body.

The trace of humor in Rafe's voice came from nowhere. "Read that in a book, didn't you?" he asked amiably.

"You are *not* going to spank him!"

"Seems to me I read that same book in a lit class my junior year in high school," he continued gently. "The guy was a Canadian mountie or something? Only these aren't quite the same circumstances. I'd know that little boy's fanny any time over yours, and I'm not about to lay a hand on you. On him—you can bet your sweet petunias."

"The heck you are!"

"Zoe. Try to relax." He set her gently, firmly in the hall, and then quietly closed the door in her face.

* * *

Both boys were in bed by nine. A half-hour before they went upstairs, Zoe had watched Aaron climb on Rafe's lap and regale him with a story about a lost puppy. She'd watched Rafe listen, and she'd watched Aaron laugh. Rafe had toted both giggling boys upside-down to bed and nobody was stingy with the good-night hugs.

Which was all very well. The urchins might take spankings for granted, but Zoe certainly didn't, and nothing was about to subdue her growing fury.

When the kids were finally asleep, Rafe went for a walk, and Zoe settled in the living room, stiffly turning the pages of a book she had no interest in. Another half-hour passed before she heard the back door opening.

He was rubbing cold hands together when he appeared in the living room. His dark hair was glistening with snow, and his cheeks were ruddy from his walk. He sent one quick look in her direction, and then crossed to the fireplace. He wasn't smiling, but the patient expression on his face was darn near enough to make her want to hit him.

He bounced down on his haunches and started stacking logs on the hearth. "I had major hopes you'd cool down, but I can see that you're still mad. Okay, let's hear it," he said quietly.

"You bet you will! I think that was one of the most cruel, insensitive, heartless, unfair—"

"Honey. I laid three quick ones on his backside. I realize from his yells you must have thought I was killing him, but you can't seriously believe I would have harmed a hair on his head." Rafe held a match to the fire and then turned to look at Zoe.

"That's not the point. He was crying! And you didn't even let me go in to him afterward—"

"There's no point to a spanking if someone cuddles him two seconds later."

His calmness only further infuriated her. "How *could* you? He just lost his parents. He's having a terrible time believing they're even gone. So he threw a lousy book. We're all he's got, and he goes and makes one tiny little mistake—"

Rafe shook his head despairingly. *"Little?* That was a three-hundred-dollar lamp, he could have set the house on fire—and we're really going to have to do something about this cold-blooded streak of yours. Want some wine?"

"No."

He sighed. "Look, honey. I loved Janet like a sister, but she coddled those kids way too much. Jonathan was my best friend, and there's no question that he took his role as father very seriously. But haven't you noticed that the monsters are a teeny bit spoiled?"

"I don't care if they're spoiled. They need love," Zoe said furiously.

"I agree with you, but that doesn't answer my question."

"You have to consider what the kids are going through right now!"

He nodded. "I did. I thought they needed to know that in a world turned upside down, there's still somebody in control. There are still rules they can count on. I wanted to give them the security of knowing that some actions are acceptable and others are dead wrong."

His words sank in. Zoe could feel her fury abating as a confusing moodiness replaced it. He not only sounded sure, but he sounded right as well. The kids did need order. And suddenly she could think of a dozen times when they'd probably been testing her, demanding limits, rules . . . and she'd failed to provide them. It had never once occurred to her that rules might mean security for them.

While she was staring at the fire, Rafe came up behind her. With a firm, sure touch, he probed the knots of tension in her shoulders. At that first contact, she flinched away, but he paid no attention. She was getting a back rub. He really didn't care whether she wanted it or not.

Flames licked a circle around the biggest log on the grate, and hot orange sparks soared up the chimney. His nostrils inhaled the sweet cherry-wood smoke as his fingers relentlessly kneaded and probed and soothed. She didn't want to relax. Her silhouette danced in the shadows on the far wall, so small next to his. Her slim shoulders and delicate profile emphasized that she was fragile and the splash of damp lashes on her cheeks showed that she was vulnerable. He knew damn well Zoe wanted to be neither.

But she wasn't moving away.

He applied pressure to her shoulders to get her to sit down. That quickly, she coiled up again. "Come on, Zoe," he scolded. "Is the world going to cave in if you relax?"

Maybe. All she really knew was that the weariness of a long, traumatic day was catching up with her. Feeling helpless, she eased down on her knees next to the crackle and warmth of the fire. She didn't want the comfort of his long, strong hands on the nape of her neck. Or maybe she did. Maybe she wanted it far too much.

She sighed helplessly. "Rafe, I don't know what the right thing to do was."

"Neither did I. That's what I've been trying to tell you, Zoe. That I can't handle this alone any more easily than you can. This parent business is exhausting," he murmured wryly.

"Maybe we should get them some books?"

"Maybe we should forget about children for a while."

"I can't."

Rafe's eyes softened. "I know you can't. So let's talk about them indirectly. Tell me about the man who was in your life. He wanted kids, didn't he? Is that why you broke off with him?"

"I never said . . . I never told you—"

"So tell me now," he said quietly. "Why not?"

He sat on the floor and pulled her down in front of him, his thighs bracing hers while he continued to rub her back. A gentle massage wouldn't do. Her slender spine was so knotted up with little coils that he was tempted to wrap her up in his arms and kiss her until every thought of children permanently vanished from her head . . . but that wouldn't do, either. For now, he wanted to listen. He needed to listen.

When he found the taut cord at the nape of her neck, she lifted her head. He firmly pushed it back down again, and discovered that Zoe was a helpless sucker for a scalp rub. Her silky hair curled around his fingers, catching gold lights from the fire. In time, loosening all those tight muscles seemed to loosen her tongue as well.

She told him how sympathetic her parents had been after her hysterectomy, and how she'd come to the point where she'd had to reject that sympathy. Pity wasn't going to help her put her world back together. She'd thought Steven would.

"You loved him?" He stopped rubbing only once, to lean forward and add another log to the fire.

"Yes." Her head was bent low over her raised knees.

"But he wanted kids."

"Naturally he wanted kids." She added wearily, "Men seem to feel it's macho to appear footless and ready to pursue a brief affair, but they have the same nesting urges that women have. When it comes down to the bottom line, men want a home, a wife, and kids. It's no different for them than it is for women."

"In other words, the bastard split on you." Rafe couldn't keep the sharp coldness from his tone.

"He wasn't a bastard!"

He paid for hitting that nerve. Her eyes snapped open, and her shoulders grew tight; he had to work on those muscles all over again. In time, she calmed down . . . in direct proportion to his tensing up. Thigh-to-thigh contact had already contributed to an unavoidable male response, but now he found his jaw clenched and his arms and shoulders coiled as tightly as a bowstring. *Leave it alone*, he told himself. Only he couldn't. "You still love him?"

She didn't answer that.

"Look, Zoe. He was a damned fool. It's not as if the two of you didn't have any other options—like adopting kids if he was so hot on—Never mind, never mind! Forget I said anything."

When her lips parted, he gently shoved her head

down again, discovering he didn't want to hear her defend the bastard. He also didn't want her tense. When his fingers gently kneaded her scalp again, she arched like a kitten in the sun. That was how he wanted her. Free to be soft and lazy. Easy, sleepy, safe.

Out-of-control protective urges rushed through him. All he could think of was that her attitude toward kids made sense now. She felt she had to avoid men who liked children. The ability to have kids had been taken away from her, and that trauma had been followed by the emotional blow of rejection by a creep who had led her halfway to the altar and then ditched her as if he'd discovered she was a mutant.

He meant to shut up and stay shut up, but, dammit, he couldn't. His tone had a gruff scrape to it that he just couldn't help. "That bastard didn't leave you with the idiotic notion that being unable to have kids meant no man would ever love you, did he?"

"Rafe, stop talking about him that way. Our breakup was as much my fault as his, and I . . ." When his hands stopped massaging, it was as if he'd broken a magic spell. She was barely aware of what she'd said or of why they'd been talking about Steven. Rafe's touch had mesmerized and comforted her after a terrible day, but Zoe had never been one to allow herself the excuse of extenuating circumstances. She pushed back her tangled hair and gave a quick laugh. "Look, I'm sorry for bending your ear like this. Steven and I parted a long time ago; it's not your problem, and—"

Rafe wasn't listening. "He must have made you feel totally inadequate. No wonder you're uptight on the subject of kids."

"Of course he didn't. I told you, it wasn't all his fault. For heaven's sake—"

Too fast, he swiveled her around so she was facing him. Not expecting the quick move, she felt suddenly disoriented, and a two-second glance at Rafe's face was all it took to tell her he was angry. His brows formed a grooved furrow, and his eyes snapped like the facets of a sapphire. The fire illuminated his rigid jaw and the compressed line of his mouth, but his voice came out soft and husky. "You don't still love him. But maybe we'd better make absolutely sure you know that."

She knew what he intended. She saw his blue eyes coming for her, and she saw his lips parting to take hers. It was like watching an avalanche headed her way with all the escape routes blocked. When she tried to duck her head, his fingers anchored her chin. When she tried to rise, his arms surrounded her and the pressure of that first kiss scolded her for even trying to escape.

Her body had a small problem: It still felt like a marshmallow from all his soothing caresses. Limbs that normally obeyed mental commands simply didn't want to work just now. Her common sense seemed suddenly to have taken a vacation to Tahiti. She knew better than to allow him to kiss her. She'd sampled Rafe's kisses the night before, and her pulse rate signaled that she was in danger . . . only the danger tasted so delicious.

She stopped struggling, only because a temporary submission was better than an awkward argument. As it happened, the mental fib wasn't necessary. It wasn't a simple submission Rafe wanted at all. Kiss followed kiss until she was breathless, until the snap of the fire sounded like a roar in her ears, until her arms were tightly wrapped around him and her fingers were laced in his hair. Responding to him wasn't a matter of choice. She only wished it were.

When he finally lifted his head, the anger had disappeared from his expression. His eyes intimately searched hers, and whatever he saw there aroused the trace of a smile. Still, his low voice had an edge. "Don't ever peg me on the same hook with him, Zoe. Children don't matter to me; they've never mattered to me. It's damned hard to find someone to talk to, someone you want to wake up to in the morning, someone who'll still be there if you make a mistake. If and when a man finds someone like that, he'd be a damn fool to let her go. Believe me, you don't still love him."

Loving Steven wasn't an issue, and she would have told Rafe that if he'd give her the chance. He didn't. When his hands slid under her shirt, she shuddered. His palm stroked one breast until the tip hardened and her eyes closed, and his lips labeled the pulse at her throat "his." The hollow above her collarbone was treated to a similar branding.

Any minute now, her heart was going to stop quaking. Tenderness and excitement didn't go together like this. A man couldn't be both fierce and tender. And a woman couldn't possibly feel both helpless and superlatively, powerfully, exultantly female.

"You felt like this with him? As though the whole world were burning up? Do you know how you make me feel when you respond like this?"

"Rafe, stop . . ." *Talking*. She didn't want to hear; she didn't want to think. If he was trying to tell her he wanted her, he was making himself crystal clear. If he was trying to banish the thought of any other man from her mind, he was doing a good job of that, too. Steven had taught her something about need; Rafe was teaching her about a maelstrom of need. He made her feel as if she'd just discovered desire. He could make a woman believe she would die if she didn't have him.

When he eased her down to the carpet, she welcomed its cushioning support in a world that was rapidly becoming blurred, indistinct, without edges. Her whole body tightened when his thigh slid between hers. His tightened when he impatiently released the buttons of her shirt and discovered bare skin.

Obviously, she shouldn't have let him discover bare skin. His breath was suddenly a hoarse rasp, his eyes blazed blue, and need shuddered through his body. Through the thin material of her bra, she felt his lips on her nipple, and then his tongue.

He was going too fast, much too fast. She knew every reason why this was wrong, and couldn't care. Maybe for too long she'd refused to believe that a man could want just Zoe, just the woman, not for what she could give or produce but for who she was. Maybe it was different because he was Rafe—patient always, but not now. Easy and slow always, but not now. Logical and rational always, but at the moment he couldn't seem to manage the simple catch of a bra, and he kissed her like he was damn-well starved.

"Touch me, Zoe. Do you want me to go crazy?"

Was that the question of a rational man? "Rafe." She managed to capture both his hands before they burned her up with a touch that was hotter than fire. "If you give me a chance, I will," she murmured softly.

He opened glazed eyes on her smile. Whatever he saw made him momentarily still. Her tumbled hair was catching the glow of firelight, and his fingers reached up to touch it, and while he was busy with that she raised her lips to his. She offered him a woman's kiss, a woman's wooing, soft, exploring, a sharing of promises. Her fingers strayed over his forehead, his cheekbones, the line of his jaw.

"You know this isn't wise, don't you?" she whispered, but she didn't stop. The pulse in his Adam's apple leaped when she traced it with her forefinger. She opened the top button of his shirt, and then the next and the next. His chest was smooth and brown and warm to her touch.

"This isn't wise," she echoed, but sensations kept flooding her, and wisdom was easily jettisoned. She felt brazen and desirable and joyful. She hadn't voluntarily touched a man in three years. She couldn't. The right to be loved was inexorably linked, in her mind, to her right to love, to come to a man as a whole woman. For three years, she'd felt like apologizing to every man she met for being flawed. Not with Rafe. When Rafe touched her, she felt infinitely whole, deliciously powerful as a woman. Her lips brushed his heartbeat with sweet abandon.

"Stop me, Rafe," she whispered. All of it was illusion. It had to be. Maybe she just wanted to believe with this man it was different. Touch was only going to complicate her life and his. She knew that, but she couldn't seem to stop. Her own needs led the dance she'd thought she'd never know again.

"So precious, Zoe. You're so precious . . ." His palm slid down her side to her hip. He molded her length to his, kisses falling on her nose, her cheeks, her closed eyes.

"Hi."

Rafe instantly turned to stone at the sound of the sleepy soprano.

"Whatcha doing?" Parker asked interestedly. His pajama bottoms sagging, he had one foot propped on the other in the doorway.

"We were..." Rafe took a rapid breath. He turned eyes glazed with horror on Zoe, but only for a second. In the next second, his hands were groping for her shirt. "I was...Snookums had a small hurt. I was fixing it."

"Daddy did that for Mommy all the time."

"Did he?"

Parker nodded. "He kissed her to make it better. Mommy did that for us, too. Except that most of the time she kissed our hurts on the kitchen counter. Daddy always took Mommy into the bedroom on Sunday mornings while we were supposed to be—"

"I get the picture," Rafe said rapidly. He shot Zoe another look, an interesting blend of murderous frustration and mild amusement. She was too busy climbing back to the real world to ponder it. He was having problems closing the blouse over her breasts, mostly because his hands were distinctly unsteady. Finally, he appeared satisfied and straightened up.

He pushed a hand through his hair and stared for several seconds as if the child were a Martian. "Did you want something?"

The urchin nodded. "I'm thirsty."

"Thirsty." Rafe repeated the word as if he'd never heard it before. "Thirsty?"

"I'm milk thirsty. Not water thirsty. Otherwise—"

"You could have gotten it yourself." Rafe muttered

a fierce "Do *not* move, Zoe. Do not think, do not breathe, do not do *anything*," and lurched to his feet.

Thoughts began to reel through her head the instant he and Parker were out of sight. Shakily, she got to her feet and pulled her blouse closed, buttoning fast. From the kitchen, she could hear the two talking, the refrigerator door closing, a glass being set on a counter.

It wasn't long before the light flicked off in the kitchen and Rafe headed for the stairs with the little boy in his arms. Parker's head was already lying on Rafe's shoulder, and his eyelids were drooping.

Minutes later, Rafe came back downstairs. Waiting for him at the bottom of the steps, Zoe had her hands on her hips. His gaze seared on hers when he saw her expression. "You didn't do a very good job of staying put," he said softly.

"We both knew that either of them could have woken up at any time. And we were right there in plain sight on the living room carpet."

"Yes," he murmured. "And the wonder of it is that you forgot about the kids for a few minutes."

"Rafe—"

"Yes, I heard you. We were way out of line." He took the last step down, blocking her path to the stairway. Gently, he brushed her hot cheeks with his knuckles. "We'll have to be more careful about choosing a time and place."

"No," she said simply.

He didn't pretend any confusion about what she was saying no to. "It *will* happen again," he said quietly. "I think you know that."

She shook her head and stared at the blur just

beyond his shoulder. To look in his eyes was to see things she didn't want to see. To be touched by him was to feel things she shouldn't feel. She took a breath. "If this happens again, I'll leave. They're better off with you anyway, Rafe; surely you can already see that?"

All he could see was that she ran scared whenever kids came into the picture. Time. He desperately needed time with her. "You can't leave," he said swiftly.

"I can."

"But you wouldn't, Zoe," he said softly. "You wouldn't leave the children stranded with me unless you were absolutely sure they'd be happy here. You agreed to give it three weeks in my place and another three at yours. I intend to hold you to that. At the end of that time, we'll agree about where they're better off, but you've got to give—" He almost said "the two of us," and immediately corrected that. "You've got to give them that much time."

She searched his eyes a long time before she said quietly, "You're right. I won't leave you stranded," and sighed. "Rafe, we've both been thrown into this situation against our will, so maybe it's natural for us to need each other, to turn to each other. And maybe we got temporarily carried away, but we're not going to be together permanently. One of us is going to have the kids. The other one isn't. And to start something—"

Rafe's palms framed her face, forcing her to meet his eyes. "Nothing's going to happen that you don't want. No one's going to push you into anything you can't handle. Believe me?"

"No."

Humor glinted in his blue eyes. For two cents, he'd kiss that stubborn chin until it melted. "Maybe you can believe something that's far more important, then," he whispered. "A man scraped your emotions pretty raw because he wanted a mother for his kids. You can be damned sure that what I feel for you has nothing to do with children. *Any* children."

"That isn't the point."

"Yes, it is. I want you for *you*, Zoe. And what the two of us feel for each other is the only thing that matters."

There was just no talking to him. Zoe shot him a look, and then ducked under his arm and hurried up the stairs. Inside his bedroom, she leaned back against the closed door, feeling her breath come quick and uneasy in the darkness.

Rafe was clearly an irrational man. Any sane human being would see that a relationship was impossible because of the kids. It was sheer selfishness for them to think of each other when they had to do what was right for the children.

Eventually, she moved away from the door and burrowed under the bed covers. And eventually, it occurred to her that, like a total idiot, she was lying there fully dressed. She pushed herself back up, rid herself of her clothes, and tugged on a nightgown. Between soft sheets and the warm weight of a comforter again, she discovered her hands were annoyingly cold and trembly.

It seemed she was capable of being as irrational as Rafe. When he touched her, she felt as if she'd found something she'd thought irretrievably lost, the quality of feeling whole and good about herself and free and just . . . a woman. She wanted that feeling. She so badly wanted the man. In his arms, she'd never once thought of the kids.

Two people naturally turned to each other when they were thrown together in an emotional situation. That was all that was going on. She knew better than to involve herself in a relationship with a man who needed her only to care for children. She would never be sure she was loved for herself. And as far as the kids went, everything that had happened since they'd arrived had shown her she had no ideal-mother potential whatsoever.

She had to think of the twins. In her heart, she knew they would be better off with Rafe. *Kids don't matter to me, Zoe. They've never mattered to me.* Yes, she'd heard that, but she also saw how he was with them. His job, his house, his whole life would be affected when he took the children; naturally, he felt unsure about his ability to handle it. He needed time. He was such terrific father material. He just didn't know it yet.

Punching the pillow, Zoe settled down and determinedly closed her eyes. She'd stay because she had to stay. She'd stay until he saw how precious the twins were, and with time she had no doubt that would happen. The only thing that couldn't happen was her falling in love with him.

Except that in the darkness, in the silence, she was terribly afraid that it had already happened.

CHAPTER SIX

THE NEXT NIGHT, as soon she came downstairs after putting the boys to bed, Rafe was waiting for her at the bottom of the stairs with two pool cues in his hand. The balls had been racked, the game ready to play. They played, Zoe's nerves hammering, but he never said a word about stakes or total dominion, nor did he protest when she announced that three games were enough and she was going to bed.

The next night, he set up a Trivial Pursuit board. The night after that, they watched a movie on television. She would have gone to sleep immediately afterward if Rafe hadn't heated up two mugs of mulled cider and brought them into the living room. And Thursday night she was so tired; the boys had been pistols all day. Rafe insisted that she go for a walk with him. The night was pirate-black and crisp and special; starlight sparkled on snow. He never touched her.

He just talked and made her talk. Not about kids. Once a day, he affirmed that there was no possible way he could handle the children without her, but after that, the subject of kids was banned. They discussed more important issues. Like how many whimsical hats she owned. Whether Bogart or Tracy was the best actor of the forties. How serious her allergy to clams was. How many stars filled the night sky. How many feet there were in a fathom.

Gradually, against her will, she could feel her pulse leaping as soon as the kids were in bed. Knowing she'd be with Rafe was like the promise of an ice-cream sundae after a sweltering day. Even during the most harrowing hours with the fractious twins, she knew relief was coming. He'd seen reason . . . she was so glad. She needed him as a friend, and he was such a good friend; any deeper emotional relationship would have cluttered up everything, and she was relieved that he finally saw that.

Today, though, she was having a small problem.

She tried again to free her hand from Rafe's. He wasn't exactly holding her hand like a handcuff or a vise or a chain, but every time she tried to ease her fingers free from his, his grip tightened.

This morning he'd suggested bringing the boys to see his lab. It had seemed like a terrific idea. It still *seemed* that way. The boys were talking ten for a dozen; Sarah and another of Rafe's co-workers were in the room; and his lab was frankly as conducive to romantic feelings as a bucketful of dead fish.

"And this laser-ranging instrument is my baby, Zoe..."

Dutifully, she inspected his laser-ranging equipment, then his magnetometer, tiltmeter, scintillation counter, and the dozen other technical tools of his trade. A sane woman did not respond to such an environment like a nymphomaniac to a free bed. A sane woman did not come apart at the seams simply because a man was holding her hand.

"We don't face much danger of major quakes here, but the potential for disaster from a small earthquake in snow country is incredible. The smallest tremor can set off an avalanche of dangerous proportions. And in the past twenty years, populations have increased around ski resorts to such an extent that..."

Yes. She heard him, but she couldn't seem to seriously listen. A lock of hair drooped boyishly over his forehead. He talked about his work with his hands, with his smile, with a vitality and fascination that spilled over into his voice. His jeans fit just right this morning; he was wearing a yellow and gray plaid shirt that revealed the shape of his shoulders and chest.

"...so the information we're gathering here can be used in the Alps, in Aspen, at the California ski areas. Wherever fault lines..."

"Yes," she murmured obediently. But she already knew about fault lines. The major source of her personal earth tremors had misled her all week into believing she was safe. How could she be less than safe here in his lab, where he was showing the boys his work? And she was so sure she'd drilled personal feelings right out of her head and substituted concern about childcare instead.

The boys finally detached themselves from Sarah in the far corner and bounded toward them. "Uncle Rafe, we're hungry," Parker announced.

Her heart warmed at the way they looked at Rafe. On every occasion when she'd tried to discuss the kids, he'd expressed increasing doubts about his ability ever to handle them, and then he'd cut her off. He needed more time, she kept thinking . . . but the urchins didn't realize that. Parker already knew he could count on Rafe even if the whole rest of the world fell apart. Aaron sidled up to Rafe for the hug or casual squeeze he knew was coming—Aaron craved those touches. Whether Rafe realized it or not, he knew instinctively what each child needed.

Really, it wasn't strictly her fault she couldn't stop falling in love with the man.

Once the children claimed his attention, though, she had the sense to remove her hand from his. "I'll take them home for lunch," she said swiftly. "We never meant to take up this much of your morning. I know you're busy—"

"Not too busy for a picnic lunch with you and the boys. Sarah?" Rafe motioned to let her know they were leaving, and then gave Zoe a pensive frown. "You're not exactly going to fit into my spare snowmobile suit."

She raised both eyebrows. "Is that supposed to be a major worry in my life?"

"Of course it is. You need to dress warmly if we're going sledding."

"What? And I don't know what you meant about a picnic, but someone should have mentioned to you that it's snowing outside."

"Yes."

"And this is a workday for you."

"Yes."

"And I'm taking the boys home for lunch."

Poor Zoe, she still didn't understand. Rafe zipped her into the huge old snowsuit she didn't want to be zipped into, and had the boys in giggling fits when he had to fold and refold the cuffs to make it even marginally fit. He jammed a hat on her head and tucked in her hair possessively. She didn't like that either.

"There is a *lot* of snow outside," Zoe remarked.

"Hmmm?"

"Picnics are for hot summer days. You need ants and lemonade for picnics. You need watermelon. You need sunshine." It was like trying to explain to a brick wall. "I have lunch all ready for them at home . . ."

"Boys?" Rafe turned to the children. "Do you want to go home to plain old peanut butter, or do you want to cook hot dogs in the snow?"

On cue, the unanimous verdict was "Hot dogs in the snow! Come *on*, Snookums!"

She gave in—only because of the boys, of course. Rafe felt a moment's guilt for using the urchins to win an argument, but it didn't last long. Over the past week, he'd discovered that she was seriously prepared to play this silly "we can be friends" routine forever. He'd hoped that by defusing a little sexual tension, he could help her build trust and confidence in him, make her see that they had something special between them. But Zoe could apparently hide behind her best perky smiles and keep her distance from him forever if he let her. Which he wouldn't.

It was a sun-dazzled day. Rafe parked the jeep just off the road in a stand of snow-laden trees. Just beyond

the heavy firs lay a long sloping hill, crusty with the
sun's diamonds and ideal for sledding. He'd found the
private retreat months before. Ever since she'd come
here, he'd wanted to share it with Zoe.

"Does it strike you even the least little bit that this is
slightly nuts?" she asked politely.

It struck him very strongly that Zoe was the most
giving woman he'd ever met. As far as he could see,
she never took from anyone. Once she realized the kids
wanted the picnic, she'd never seriously hesitated. If
they wanted the Nile, he figured she'd probably have
the river shipped from Egypt. She fussed with things,
like putting a spoonful of sugar in his coffee for him
when he could obviously do it himself. Bickering kids
were herded out of his sight—she thought she was
making sure he saw only the best side of the boys. What
he saw was that she had the gift of caring for people,
smoothing over all the rough spots a person could en-
counter in a day.

He'd never once caught her thinking of herself. And
an example of that was now. From the back of the jeep,
she was loading her arms with the tarp, hot dogs, buns,
two thermoses . . .

"Zoe?" he asked patiently.

She turned back.

"I really think I could carry a little something."

"I don't mind—oh, look at them, Rafe!" The boys
were making angels in the snow and laughing, all
red-cheeked. When her face tilted back toward him,
her smile was mystically sweet and her eyes dancing.
"*How* are we going to make a fire in the snow?"

"*We* aren't going to do anything. I'm going to
make the fire, and you're going to practice doing ab-

solutely nothing." He reached up to touch her cheek. She never moved away from his touch; she just looked at him as though he were an overgrown puppy who hadn't learned to behave himself yet. "You're here to play," he informed her.

"That's all I do, play all day. I can build a fire. If you—"

He took the gear from her and dropped it, then motioned her firmly toward the boys with a forefinger.

She propped her hands on her hips. "What is this macho nonsense? I'm not exactly helpless, you know."

"Pity," he murmured.

He was making her darned nervous, and she really had no intention of enjoying herself, but somehow it happened. Cold air burned her cheeks, and snow fell around her like confetti; she should have felt foolish in the oversized snowsuit, but somehow she didn't. Building the little fire was fun, because they were all part of it; the twins raved over the burned hot dogs and so did Zoe. Rafe had brought one thermos of soup and another of hot cider. Veal cordon bleu and champagne couldn't have tasted better.

With her fingers wrapped around the cider mug and her legs curled under her, she watched the kids shake branches and chortle when mountains of snow tumbled down on them. At home, she would have been worried about spills and spats. Outside like this, there was nothing to worry about. With Rafe around, nothing bad was going to happen.

"Zoe . . ."

Her eyes swiveled to meet his across the last of the

spitting, bright fire. His snowsuit was open at the throat; he didn't seem to feel the cold. His smile was warm, and the irony of the situation swamped her. With Rafe, she felt safe. With Rafe, she also felt as if she were sitting on rotten timbers. A logical woman couldn't possibly feel both sensations in equal measure, and she was extraordinarily grateful when the boys came hurtling toward them.

"*When?*" Aaron demanded for the fifteenth time.

"I thought you promised to give us a full five minutes to finish our lunch," Rafe reminded him.

"We've given you hours," Parker said sternly. "We were done with lunch practically yesterday. What's taking you guys so long?"

"Digestion," Rafe murmured, but he stood up with a long-suffering expression that made Zoe laugh. "I should have settled for just lunch instead of mentioning the sleds," he whispered darkly.

"I saw the hill," she told him.

"It's long."

"And both sleds look heavy."

Her first time down the hill, she tipped over the sled, rolled twenty feet, and came up laughing. In seconds, all three males in her life were there to dust her off. The next time, she went down with Aaron on her back, and the third time she took both laughing boys, who insisted they could win a race against Uncle Rafe only if they had "ballast"—a new word for the day, and one they repeated over and over as if it were magic.

"More ballast, Snookums. More ballast!"

"Uncle Rafe's beating us! If he wasn't so ballaster—"

On her fourth trek up the hill, she was still laughing, heaven knew why. Snow had crept down her neck, she'd lost her hat, and every leg muscle protested the fierce climb. Still, the boys were so obviously happy. Rafe's hideaway was so crystal-lovely, so private and special. And uncomplicated fun hadn't been part of her life in so long.

At the top of the hill, Rafe announced, "All right. The big kids against the little ones this time. Parker and I will be on the bottom. Zoe, you climb on top of me, and Aaron, you climb on top of Parker. Last one down the hill is the last one to get cider!"

She should have known. She *did* know that climbing on top of Rafe wasn't the wisest of choices, but this was sledding, and they were just playing, and there were pounds of clothes between them.

They took off at a racing speed that sent snow stinging in her face and made her stomach thrill for the ride, but there was suddenly more. There was having to hold on to him, and an awareness of the length of him beneath her. The chemistry that had been on hold suddenly exploded in a burst of exhilaration. Dammit, did she have to love being near him?

"*Keel!*" he suddenly yelled.

Keel? "What?"

"The trees! Damna—"

As far as she could tell, he deliberately threw her off the sled. She landed on a sun-crusted patch of sheer ice that sent her sliding several feet. When she finally stopped, stars were dancing in front of her eyes in broad daylight. Snow was everywhere—in her mouth, in her hair, in her eyes.

"You're all right?" Rae was beside her in seconds. He knelt down and ripped off his glove. Cold, firm fingers brushed the snow from her face and hair.

"I'm . . . fine." She thought she was, anyway.

"We wiped out. Damned trees," he said disgustedly.

She laughed. "I thought we were flying. Maybe Parker's right about your being 'ballaster.' Don't blame the trees, you big lug."

She wasn't sure what happened then. She was trying to rise, and he was still brushing the snow from her cheeks. His face suddenly blocked the sunlight, and she saw his eyes. What had been clear and bright became hazy and soft. A cold day turned hot. And there was no one there on earth but the two of them.

She never saw the kiss coming. His lips were suddenly there, cool and smooth on hers, in total contrast to the damp warmth of his tongue. He took no time for a tentative exploration, but claimed, now, with a hunger that wouldn't wait, an urgency as naked and bold as a man's desire.

The sun shone in her eyes and she had to close them. For hours, her whole body had been geared up for energy; suddenly, every muscle and pore felt sapped of will, languid and lazy. He was a thief. A kiss thief. A man who'd take advantage of a woman when she was down, and she had no excuse for letting her arms slide around his neck. The tumble must have addled her wits, but his breath was so clean and fresh. His need touched something so purely feminine inside her. . .

"Snookums was hurt pretty bad, right?" Parker's tone was knowing, as sage as an old-timer's.

Rafe's head lifted just inches from hers. He didn't appear to notice either boy. His eyes swept over her face, her lips. "She had the wind knocked right out of her," he confirmed. "My best guess is that she needs lots of kisses."

Both boys were familiar with the therapy. Shortly thereafter, Zoe was drowned in kisses—most of them wet smackers delivered enthusiastically from very small lips. Above the boys' heads, she could still see Rafe looking at her. She'd had the wind knocked out of her, all right.

Carting sleds and picnic gear back to his jeep, she would have avoided looking at him altogether if he hadn't grabbed her arm. "Where's my lecture about not behaving myself?" he murmured.

She shook her head.

His look was watchful, even wary. "You're starting to see?" he asked softly. "You *must* see, Zoe. We have something special between us. I'm not going to let it go. I don't think you even want me to let it go. We'll find some way to work out everything else." At her continued silence, he released a harsh sigh. "Dammit, what are you thinking?"

"That the children must be beginning to believe I'm accident-prone," she said mildly, and turned away from him to climb into the jeep.

Arguing with him was pointless. He really didn't seem to understand that the closer he got to the children, the more impossible a relationship was for the two of them. He was a born father. Day by day, she was increasingly aware that she was less than an adequate mother in instincts and judgment. She was too constantly afraid of doing wrong, too afraid the complex emotional baggage from her past would affect the kids in a negative way. Those feelings weren't going away but only intensifying as she was thrown together with them day after day. Rafe always did the right thing. She always seemed to do the wrong one.

Loving him couldn't make any difference. She wouldn't let it. The children had to come first, and the best thing for them was obviously Rafe. Just Rafe. Not Rafe and flawed Zoe.

She wanted to be home. She so badly wanted to be home. In a couple of weeks, she could be there. She'd be able to hear the gulls and smell the sea. In Washington, she'd feel more rational. She'd built a fine life around her whales and her friends and her apartment, a life that so carefully didn't include children. Or a man who came with kids.

Rafe would have her believe he needed and wanted her. What he really needed and wanted was a strong woman prepared to climb mountains with him. She wasn't that woman. Once upon a time, yes; once upon a time, she'd had an ego healthy enough to believe she was really something, and that a little curve life threw her was not going to get her down. It *had* gotten her down, from the time she'd hurt Steven. To risk being less than adequate as a mother—and to risk failing Rafe as a woman—those were risks she simply couldn't take.

From snow to sea was a heady transition. The jet, the rented car, and, last, the ferry, had brought her home to her island in Puget Sound. Zoe's pulse pounded exuberantly those last miles. If she couldn't see them yet, she could imagine the grape-winged gulls soaring overhead in search of their dinner, the jeweled colors of a sunset over the roar and pound of waves, the smell and flavor of a Pacific salt wind.

There'd been some question in her mind whether she'd survive the last two weeks in Montana. The answer was obvious. She had, and she was here. Home, where everything would be fine. She stole a glance at Rafe as he whisked a napping Aaron off her lap to carry him up to her door. In a denim jacket, the salt wind tangling in his hair, Rafe looked element-ally male, and the tight-lipped look he shot her was unmistakably irritated.

Anger, she thought fleetingly, was really a marvel-ous emotion. The next best thing to chicken soup for curing a few difficult aches and pains. When a man was angry, he kept his distance. In the meantime, she had absolutely no doubt he was growing attached to the kids, and she was home.

"Come on, Parker. Can you carry this little box for me?"

"This is where you live?" Parker was busy staring all around him. Her place was an old, huge, white-frame house that had been converted to three apart-ments. Two chestnuts and a fat cottonwood shaded the lawn, and a totally unorganized garden of lady's slippers and primroses and morning glories sprawled around the edges of the yard. "But where are your whales, Snookums? I've been waiting and waiting."

"They're a little too big to keep in the apartment, sweetheart." Par for the course, she had her arms loaded before she thought to take the key out of her purse.

"Where are the mountains?"

"Sorry, love, I don't have mountains."

"No snow either?" Parker asked mournfully.

"No snow either," she had to confirm. It stung, just for an instant, that the boys could never like her place as much as Rafe's. But then she reminded herself that that was exactly what she wanted, for all three males to realize that they were happier in Montana. "There's a park a few blocks away, though, and a movie theater. Seawind isn't a very big town, but we're close by the water. You can collect stones and shells and stuff . . ."

At last she found the key and slid it into the lock. Jay, who lived in the upstairs apartment, had promised to take care of her plants and make sure there was milk in the refrigerator when she returned. She'd done the same for him when he'd vacationed, but still, she suddenly couldn't remember exactly what shape she'd left the place in, and her eyes jumped up to Rafe's again.

"It's nowhere as large as your house," she warned. "You have to remember that when I left here, I didn't know I was coming back with three extra people. I can't imagine where we're going to fit everyone . . ."

As they all stepped inside, she rambled on. Paying no attention, Rafe took the heavy box she'd insisted on carrying, and then grabbed the suitcase before she could reach for it. The woman was driving him nuts, which she damn well knew. Radiating confidence, wearing a sassy smile, blithe as a spring breeze, she could probably benefit from a slight shaking. The problem was that he could never stay angry with her for long.

Zoe was a master of stubbornness. Arguing with

her was like fighting with the wind: The gusts just
kept coming, strong, cool, and relentless. He'd argued with her when he'd found her rocking Aaron at
four in the morning. He'd argued with her when
she'd claimed *she*'d broken the needle on his stereo,
when very obviously Parker had done it, and Rafe
didn't care about the damn thing anyway. He'd argued with her over spending part of her life's savings
on childrens' books.

She was wearing herself out caring for the twins,
but he couldn't make her see it. She refused to recog-
nize that she was fantastic with them, and she'd done
her level best to get out of spending three weeks with
them on her turf. Even last night, she'd still been
arguing that there was no point in their coming here;
the kids obviously belonged with him.

Where the damn woman belonged was with him,
where he could protect her and love her and take care
of her and love her . . . and more things like that.

Instead, she figured she had everything all set.
He'd be with the monsters all day forming the attachment she was so anxious for him to feel, and she'd be
off at her job, busy being emotionally uninvolved.
He knew she felt she had to protect herself. He understood about that emotional brick wall she'd built
up. He was just at an increasing loss as to how to
convince her that he wasn't going to hurt her. All he
wanted to do was love her.

"Hold on, Geronimo!"

Both boys halted in midair with guilty expres-
sions.

"We're not going to touch *anything* until we have
Zoe's permission, are we boys?"

"Rafe, it's all right—"

"Is that clear?" he demanded of the boys.

It was clear; they even bounded off to explore at a reasonably sedate space.

"I'm afraid they'll have to sleep in a double bed. That's all I've got in the spare room."

"It'll do just fine."

"I don't have that much closet space. I'll move things to make space for your clothes just as soon as—"

"Yes," he clipped out, but he wasn't really listening. Tossing his jacket on a chair, he glanced around the room, and every ounce of irritation and frustration slowly faded from his system.

Her living room wouldn't survive a five-minute assault by the four-year-olds. She had four similar lamps. He thought they were called Tiffany-style lamps; they had stained-glass shades that gleamed like jewels when switched on. A whimsical collection of pewter candlesnuffers sat on a cherry table that had been varnished to a high gleam. Near the door stood a hat rack festooned with a dozen of those crazy hats she loved.

She must have started with a neutral color scheme —at least the couch and rug were of a muted sand color. It had been silly of her, really; bland colors weren't Zoe. A cluster of peacock feathers waved brightly from a brass umbrella stand in the corner. Fat couch pillows displayed more rainbow colors, so did a handmade afghan crocheted in bright squares. Her bookcase was another catchall for color... polished stones she must have picked up at the beach, a hand-painted cup and saucer, a crystal dangling where it caught the light. Plants hung in the windows. Maybe they'd been tame at one time, but the greenery had long since taken to sprawling wildly in search of every ray of available light. Like Zoe, who so indomitably reached for zest and life, and who was so damned sure she was happy settling for tameness and safety.

"Oh, God, it's a mess," she said distractedly, and immediately hid a crocheting bag behind the couch, started to gather up magazines.

"It's not a mess. It's just like you," he said gently.

"I'm a sucker for clutter," she agreed with a laugh, and then stood with her hands on her hips, wearing an expression he knew well. "This time, you take the bed and I'll take the couch, and I refuse to hear any arguments about it. You wouldn't fit on my couch if we sawed you off at the knees."

"True." His tone was wry.

"Well . . ." For some ridiculous reason, she suddenly felt uncertain. This was her home, where she'd always had control of her life. If Rafe would just stop looking at her with that soft smile . . . "I'd better show you where everything is," she said briskly.

She showed him everything in her coral kitchen from soup bowls to peanut butter, then revealed the secrets of her washing machine, then toured the bath and spare room where the kids would sleep. Everything went fine until they reached her bedroom, where he was going to sleep.

She slipped inside while he stayed rooted in the doorway, and that quiet smile of his blossomed into a full-fledged grin. Darn it, she'd had no time to prepare for company, and certainly not in here. With her hand behind her at the dresser, she rapidly shoved earrings, a nightgown, and bra into the drawer. "Now, I know it looks a little crowded, but the closet in the spare room is less crowded, and I'll take some of my stuff out of the drawers . . ."

He simply refused to pay attention. His gaze was dawdling over the dozen half-filled vials of perfume —she loved scent—the collection of framed butterflies on the wall, the pink satin spread with its soft fringe, the trinkets spilling out of her jewelry box.

"Know something, Zoe?" he murmured.

"What?"

His blue eyes alit on her the way a bee settles on nectar. "You're pure female right down to the smallest cell in your body."

Frustration coiled in Zoe's stomach. She was going to feel safe, sound, and immune from that man's eyes if it killed her.

CHAPTER SEVEN

"GO *ON*, YOU big ox. *Swim!* Get out of here. Scram. We're your enemies, remember?" Zoe's Institute for Orca Research had three mammoth saltwater holding tanks. At the moment the underwater gates were open on one of them. Tattered Lady and her calf were free to go, and the Pacific and freedom were waiting for them.

Five weeks before, Zoe had been a member of the institute crew that had brought in the wounded hump-back. The name Tattered Lady had been a natural. The dorsal fin had been so chewed up that the whale had been weak from loss of blood and unable to care for her young one. During Zoe's absence, Tattered Lady had been successfully nursed back to health, but the honor of freeing her had been delayed until Zoe's return . . .

only the lady was not all that excited about reentering a cold, cruel world.

Zoe had spent more than half of her first day back at work underwater in a wet suit. Dressed in street clothes now, she was weary and freezing under a typical Puget Sound mist. She crossed her ankles and all available fingers as the whale once more breached and dived in a graceful arc toward the gate. Just as smoothly, she turned and headed back inland.

"That's *freedom* out there, you big jerk," Zoe hissed with frustration. "Where's your pride? You want to be on welfare the rest of your life? You're as healthy as a horse, you big lummox. Go get your own plankton."

"You tell her, Zoe." Sandy, next to Zoe, was chuckling at Zoe's scoldings. With the ink on her bachelor of science diploma barely dry, Sandy was the youngest member of the oceanographic team. A brunette with a shy smile, she'd found a mentor in Zoe from her first day on the job. "Good to have you back," she said affectionately.

Zipping up her jacket, Zoe grinned. "Good to be back. I hear you did a terrific job while I was gone. No more horrendous teasing about being our institute rookie?"

Sandy shrugged her slight shoulders. "I expected that when I started here." She motioned toward the water. "Want me to leave the gate open overnight?"

"No. I only made that mistake once, about two years ago, and ended up with two sharks, a ray, and a school of jellyfish prepared to set up house here permanently. Tomorrow we'll bait the water outside the gate or, if worse comes to worst, lead the calf out and hope the mother follows." Zoe sighed, giving one more possessive glance at her humpback whale before grabbing her shoulder bag. "She's healed well. I had my doubts she could make it when we brought her in five weeks ago."

"Ralph says you bully them into surviving."

Zoe sent her a wry glance in shared understanding of their boss's character. "Ralph's always free with compliments, but he keeps *us* in the water and *himself* dry and warm in the lab."

"You mind if I stick close tomorrow? I'd like to help you on the echolocation project."

"Sure." Minutes later, Zoe was inside her car and headed toward home. It was barely five, yet the mist was slowly turning into a downpour that Zoe knew would mean a full-fledged fog by morning. A wildlife sanctuary bordered the institute's property. Spring was busting out on both sides of the coastal road, and any other time she would have slowed to admire the burst of violet star thistles clustered so spectacularly on her left.

Tonight she hardly noticed nature's wonders; her foot was steady on the gas pedal. She was busy feeling relief that her first day back at work had been everything she'd hoped—absorbing, challenging, satisfying.

You didn't even miss them, she told herself as she passed another car that seemed to be dawdling. She was equally certain that the three males in her life had survived beautifully without her—probably a thousand times better than if she'd been there. The boys had Rafe, they didn't need her; and heck, she'd felt as though she were being let out of prison when she'd gone to work this morning. Freedom. Lunch when she wanted it. Work she could concentrate on. Driving with both hands on the wheel instead of one adjusting a seat belt that a four-year-old had wriggled out of. Uninterrupted conversations between adults, spoken in adult language to people who'd never heard of He-Man. What more could a woman ask for?

Frustrated at a red light, she took a thorough look in four directions, discovered no other cars, and guiltily ran the light. Three blocks later she jammed on the brake in her driveway, tugged her purse strap over her shoulder, and hurled herself out of the car. Noting that Jay was offering a friendly wave from his second-floor apartment, she waved back. She knew she should stop to thank the older man for taking care of her place while she was gone, and she would . . . soon, but not now.

Belatedly aware that she was rushing hell-bent for leather for no reason at all, she slowed her pace to a sedate gallop. *It's that man's fault. Before he came into your life, you were a sane, competent, rational, sensible . . .*

. . . surprised woman, she qualified fleetingly as she opened the front door. At first glance, she wondered who was moving. Her four Tiffany-style lamps were grouped on top of the bookcase, along with her pewter candlesnuffers, her crocheting bag, and every ornament she'd ever collected—some of which she hadn't seen in years. Pillowcases were draped over her cherry-wood tables like giant doilies. Her afghan was meticulously folded over a hanger in the front hall closet. The apartment hadn't looked so neat since the last tenant had lived there. No noise, no chaos . . . no Rafe, no children . . .

Tossing her yellow felt hat on the rack, Zoe ran a hand through her hair and wandered through to the kitchen. "Where is everybody?"

Two angels with freshly brushed hair instantly scraped back chairs to barrel toward her. "Snookums!"

Her renegade heart turned over. She hadn't exactly missed them all day, she'd just . . . missed them. Terribly. Still, one good look and she could see who was the better caretaker. No sticky fingers, no signs of tears; Rafe had found a miracle cure for little boys' cowlicks, and their shirts were even tucked in! If her own particular failures at mothering assaulted her at that moment, she didn't care. She could still be an aunt, couldn't she? She could still love them.

Wet smacks delivered, they chattered thirteen to the dozen. She nodded gravely at intervals, and finally snatched a moment to look at Rafe.

Standing by the stove, he had a towel slung over his shoulder and a wooden spoon in his hand. "Good day?" he mouthed, and she nodded her reply with a sparkle of laughter for his efficient house-husband appearance, but then her smile wavered. His shirt was hanging out; he must have spent the day acquiring bags under his eyes; and his color brought to mind a man who'd just crossed a desert without food or water.

When the twins left the room, she straightened. "What happened?"

"Nothing. Just sit down and relax. Dinner's ready and waiting."

It was. His meat loaf wasn't bad, and the bakery-bought cheesecake was delicious. If Rafe didn't say much, the two boys more than made up for his reticence with steady dinner-table conversation. Aaron only tried to climb on the table once, and Zoe watched in amazement as both boys took their plates to the counter when they finished. His control . . . she'd never once had that kind of control over the children, and when dinner was over he insisted she *not* help with the dishes. "Look, for a few weeks, our roles are reversed. While I was working, you had time for that stuff. Now you're working, I'm the one with time to take over the house. You think I can't handle it just because I'm a man?"

"Of course not." She just wasn't used to that belligerent tone, not from Rafe, nor could she keep her eyes off his ravaged face. It seemed politic to cart the kids out of his sight for a bath, which naturally turned into a long, wet, noisy process. After that, she read them a story and tucked them in.

Once the kids were in bed, she wandered back out. Noting that Rafe wasn't in the kitchen, she poked her head into the living room. At first glance she saw no one there either; but then, at first glance, she hadn't thought to look down.

Six feet three inches of spread-eagled man lay prostrate on the carpet. *Wasted* was the first word that came to her mind, and laughter her first reaction, but no smile touched her lips as she looked down at him. A nameless emotion welled inside her—something vulnerable and potent and fragile.

She reminded herself of the outstanding job she'd done over the last two weeks in avoiding physical contact with him. She reminded herself that it wouldn't kill him to be a little tired. She reminded herself that his contact with the boys was exactly what was needed to create an emotional bond between them. She reminded herself of a lot of things, and then she quietly slipped off her shoes and tiptoed toward him.

Kneeling beside him, she leaned forward and gently applied her fingers to the nape of his neck. Contrary to appearances, the man was not dead. He groaned, quite loudly. She didn't find tight muscles in his neck; she found shafts of ungiving sinew and just shook her head. "All right. So tell me what happened," she ordered him.

It seemed to require a monumental amount of strength for him even to talk. "I took them grocery shopping."

"Ah."

"I will *never* make the mistake of doing that again."

"I understand." She rubbed and pulled and stretched those muscles.

"You know that park a couple blocks away?"

"Yes?"

"Aaron climbed to the top of the monkey bars and couldn't get down."

"Hmm." Who would have guessed that a big, strong man could be turned into bread dough by a simple back rub?

"After we came home, Parker locked himself in the bathroom. I had to unhinge the door to get him out."

"Hmm."

"All of your perfumes are now in the medicine cabinet. I bought a lock for it. The key's in my shoe. I couldn't think of any other safe place to hide it."

"Thank you."

"The yarn in that bag . . . They figured it would be a neat idea to turn the entire living room into a huge spiderweb and—never mind. I'll buy you some new yarn. See, when I told them it was okay, I had no idea . . . Zoe. I had *no idea*—"

"It's okay."

"I read them this story about a choo-choo train at

least forty times. Want to hear it? Because by now I'm pretty sure I've got it memorized."

"Not necessary," she assured him.

"Zoe?"

"Yes?"

"I love them. But they're animals."

"Now, Rafe. Your first day was bound to be a little tough, but I think it's possible they're just normal four-year-olds."

"Maybe. But they lie. I asked them why the curtain was down." He motioned vaguely to the curtain which was now back up. "They said it was an 'awesome miracle.' I asked them why your room smelled like a perfume factory. They said a little man with green hair had come into the house and done it. And they talk, Zoe. They talk all day. They never stop talking."

"I know," she murmured. And at that exact moment, she knew something else: it was really too late to talk herself out of loving him.

She pushed up his shirt—the material was only in the way, anyway—and let her palms roam possessively over his warm skin. Her conscience registered all the warnings she already knew. A short-term intimate relationship was impossible because of the children. And a long-term relationship was equally impossible, not just because Rafe hadn't mentioned marriage, but because marriage for the sake of the children had died out in medieval times. When and if she sought a long-term relationship, she would have to be absolutely certain that *she* mattered to him. However selfish that was, she simply couldn't survive failing in another relationship because of expectations about children that she couldn't fulfill.

So all relationships were impossible, but her hands kept kneading, and that feeling of love started in her toes and slowly filled her, engulfing her in its glow until her throat felt tight. It was the strangest thing. Sex should have been part of it. A bewilderingly strong sexual attraction had been part of her feelings for Rafe from the beginning, but hormones didn't explain that welling in her throat, the way her eyes felt tight, the sensation of soft sweetness spreading through her in lazy tentacles.

"Not there. It hurts there."

"Does it?" But she worked specifically around that vertebra where he was obviously sore.

"Zoe. I've been to Vietnam. I spent a month camping in freezing weather on a mountain in the wintertime. I was in Guatemala during the earthquake. I really don't have a major problem coping with the elements."

"I know you don't."

"So how could two small four-year-old boys—"

"I really think it's time you took me to bed," she said gently.

"—completely reduce a man to—" He stopped talking abruptly. His eyelids flew open, and he rolled over onto his back.

In time, his right hand languidly reached out and captured her wrist. He tugged her down, slowly, as if terrified of setting off a box of TNT. Just as carefully, he leaned over her, pinned her legs with one of his, and cleared his throat. Such machinations might have been enough to make Zoe smile, except that she couldn't.

A groove of a frown marred his forehead, and his eyes searched hers, roaming with intense concentration over her fragile features. He wrapped a strand of her hair around his fingers, then let it spring free . . . then did it again. "I must have heard you wrong," he said finally.

No man should have such blue eyes. "I'm pretty sure there's nothing wrong with your hearing."

"So am I."

"Of course, you could have it checked tomorrow. There's a doctor in town—"

"Look at me, Zoe."

But what she saw in his eyes made her heart pound and her hands feel shaky. He wasn't going to settle for a light and breezy tone from her, and she suddenly didn't know how to tell him that she was afraid. His lips brushed hers with the tenderest of kisses, just one. And then he lifted his head, looked at her, and reached for her hand. "Come on."

The hallway that led back to the bedrooms was really very short. Just then, it annoyingly lengthened into a long mile and a half. Still holding her hand, he popped his head into the kids' bedroom for a minute and closed their door. By then he must have been able to tell she was having a sudden attack of nervousness, because her palm was damp, but he didn't let on. In her room, without releasing her hand, he punched the lock on the door and pushed a chair in front of it. He was making so sure the kids couldn't interrupt them that she tried another smile.

All smiles seemed to be locked on the other side of her head. Her heart had been suddenly replaced by a trapped butterfly, her lips were parched enough to crack, and air was having a problem getting in and out of her lungs.

The room was dark, and that helped, but then he switched on her bedside lamp. The soft glow illuminated him as he carefully pulled down her spread and blankets. When he tossed the pillows on the floor, she felt heat travel slowly up her cheeks. The white-sheeted mattress looked too bare. And then he turned to her, and she saw those blue eyes again.

Gently, he unfastened the first button of her blouse. "So . . . are we going to be nervous?" he murmured softly.

"I'm afraid so."

"Do we want to change our minds?"

She shook her head, but she certainly didn't look down. All of her blouse buttons seemed to be undone. Firm, callused fingers pushed the garment off her shoulders.

"Are there two of us scared witless here, or is it just me?" he asked patiently.

"Blast you, Rafe," she said helplessly. "Would you stop being so darned reassuring and just kiss me?"

His brows shot up in an expression of comical surprise. That relaxed her as even his touch couldn't have. Her nervousness reflected how long it had been since she'd made love, but she felt no unwillingness. This was Rafe, a man she loved and trusted. A man she could be honest with, a man she could even be nervous with.

A man she wanted very much to make love to, and his first kiss was dangerously delicious: *Hello, Zoe, welcome to earthquake country.* Her fingers fumbled with his shirt buttons, even as she returned pressure on pressure of kiss on kiss. She pushed the shirt off his shoulders as he'd pushed off hers. Under her fingertips was a playground of warm, bare flesh.

His palms skimmed her shoulders, her spine. She felt the clasp of her bra being opened, and then that barrier was gone. Air rushed from his lungs when he felt her bare breasts crushed against him. He murmured something. If she didn't catch the exact words, the intimacy of his tone was enough to make her knees quake.

His knuckles brushed against her tummy when he unsnapped her jeans. His palms slipped inside to bare flesh, and he learned her with his hands as he languidly pushed down the denim fabric. His lips wandered from her throat to the tips of her breasts, and by the time she lay outstretched on the bed, she had no clothes on and neither did he.

When she felt him trace the scar below her navel, her fingers burrowed in his hair. He must have felt that sudden tension, because his head lifted. For a moment, he just looked at her, and then his head dipped down. He branded her right breast with a kiss, then placed another just over her heartbeat; he counted her ribs with more kisses, but that caressing trail aimed relentlessly lower. Her eyes squeezed closed when she felt his mouth on the thin silver ribbon.

The scar had no feeling; she could have sworn it had no feeling, yet when his tongue traced the line of it, she felt a shattering inside, like color exploding, like a fierce ache that was more compelling than pain.

"Don't," she whispered.

He heard her. He climbed back up her body, kiss

by kiss, and when he was face to face with her, he leaned up on an elbow. As if his heart weren't pounding nor need tearing through him, he played lazily with a strand of her hair. The thick, low whisper came from the back of his throat. *"Don't* isn't a word for lovers, Zoe, and never for us. What's yours is mine in this bed, and it goes both ways."

Her skin glowed like ivory under the lamplight. He was aware—too aware—that Zoe was only sure for the moment that she wanted him. Whatever had changed her mind, he didn't want to know. His conscience pricked him for not asking. It seemed more important—he hoped it was more important—to show her how it could be between them. He kissed the tips of her fingers, then the palm of her hand.

"I read somewhere you should never bring frustrations to bed," he murmured. "I always thought that was dead wrong, Zoe. This is the worst place I can think of to fake anything. Know that you can bring frustrations to this bed. Or fear. Or old hurts, or a damned rough day. Your scars are mine when I make love to you. I want who you are *with* me."

She touched his cheek, mesmerized by the thick fringe of black lashes that softened his eyes. The strain on his features, the sapphire sheen in his eyes, was so clearly for her. She answered him in the only way she knew how, by lifting her head and touching her lips to his.

He offered her honesty. He offered her the intimacy and allure of yielding to a man who needed her, just her. He offered her the fragile sensation that she was precious to him. He offered her the irresistible promise of being wanted without boundaries, beyond sense, above thought, past right and wrong.

She took what was hers. The right to love and be loved. She matched urgent touch for urgent touch, kiss for kiss, the heat of her body with his. Heartbeats clashed and skin kneaded skin, and she'd known from the beginning he wouldn't be a careless lover. He was never that.

When he finally claimed her body, he filled her up, engulfed her with him, with wanting, with long, lean hands and lips and the fierce cadence of heat and desire. Rafe showed no interest in basic satisfaction. He wooed her with abandon, with giving, with the uncontrollable force of an avalanche, with speed and fire and ice. He wooed Zoe, all of her, cells and pores and fingertips and toes. And even when that diamond brightness of release glowed through her on one fierce, sweet cry, she held on to those rights of loving. To that wonder of feeling loved by him, to the awe of loving him. There was the treasure.

Silent as a cat, she'd nearly reached the door when she heard Rafe's groggy "Where on *earth* do you think you're going?"

"Go back to sleep," she whispered. "It's three in the morning, Rafe. I'm just going out to the couch."

They'd both napped after making love. She'd wakened to a second fantasy of swift, strong passion, but then afterward she hadn't slept, couldn't. She knew she'd have to move away from the warm circle of his arms and return to the living room; the children would be up at six. She wasn't about to let Aaron or Parker find her and Rafe in bed together.

"Come back here," Rafe ordered in a low voice.

She shook her head, undoubtedly a motion he couldn't see in the darkness. Silently, she lifted the chair away from the door. There was no point in talking about it. For two hours, her conscience had tried to make her regret having made love with him. She regretted absolutely nothing, but the reality was that two small children made a relationship impossible. She was guilty of being foolish, but never of being a fool.

She'd just turned the knob on the door when she felt his arms swamp her from behind. Sleepy and warm, he turned her around and wrapped her up as if she were a fragile present and he were the ribbon. His chest hair tickled like a memory, and his forehead touched hers in the darkness. He hugged her, and life seemed so simple. And then his finger lifted the strap on her nightgown. "I like it better when you don't wear clothes," he said sleepily.

"This is my favorite nightgown, I'll have you know."

"Still no good, Zoe."

"No?"

"Bare is better. Your skin is better." He touched the fabric. "This is just silk."

She smiled, nuzzling just a moment more in the hollow of his throat. He smelled so sleepy and warm, so uniquely like Rafe. His whiskered cheek scraped against her forehead. "Come back to bed."

"I can't. You know I can't. The children . . ."

"At the moment, Zoe, the only one I care about is you, and you're not going out to a cold couch in the middle of the night." He added, "I'll stay awake; I'll get you up before they're up. But you're sleeping with me."

His words both warmed and disturbed her. How many thousands of times had she desperately wished for a man who wanted her more than he wanted children? Only that man couldn't be Rafe. He *had* to care about the little ones, and he had to care more about them than about her, because their future mattered so much.

Still, he wasn't an easy man to argue with at three in the morning. He led her back to bed, and then, like a man, still wasn't pleased. Her cheek had to be pressed to his shoulder, her leg anchored gently between his, the covers arranged just so. He even bullied her into closing her eyes, but she whispered, "You *can't* fall asleep."

"I won't. Zoe?"

"Hmm?"

"I love you."

"I love you, too."

"Not *that* kind of I-love-you. Not the words that get said automatically after making love. I mean I *love* you."

She didn't have to think. She didn't even have to open her eyes. "No, you don't."

"Funny, but I'm damn sure I do."

"No. It's just . . . needing each other right now. Because we've been thrown together in this situation with the kids."

"If I'd been thrown together with a three-hundred-pound battle-ax with warts because of the kids, I assure you I wouldn't be in bed with her right now."

"Thank heavens you're discriminating," she murmured, but his mood would not be lightened.

"What I feel for you has nothing to do with the children, Zoe. I'll tell you as often as I have to, until you finally believe it." Before she could answer, he'd heaved up on an elbow. Dark eyes bore down on her as he stole first one pillow and then the second from beneath her head. "Honey," he scolded gruffly, "what I would like you to do, just once, is *not* think about anyone but yourself, what *you* feel, what *you* want, what *you* need. I realize you think you're a very selfish lady—you certainly keep telling me how selfish and cold-blooded you are—so just try to be that way. Just once."

"Rafe—" Her nightgown seemed to be skimming over her head.

"I'd better confess right now that three times in a night for an old man like me might be close to a miracle. But we'll try. Someone's got to teach you to be selfish, to be greedy, to be just a little bit of a taker. The whole rest of the world mastered those vices a long time ago. It's not so hard. But you want to pay close attention, because this is a very serious test about what *you* want."

"Rafe—"

"Are you concentrating?"

There was just no talking to him.

CHAPTER EIGHT

JUST AS ZOE lifted the toothbrush to her mouth, the bathroom door was nudged open. "Morning, Snookums." Parker was still trailing his blanket.

"Morning, punkin," she replied to the wearer of the sagging teddy bear pajamas, and whisked an eye to the doorway where his sidekick stood.

"Morning, Snookums." Aaron yaned.

"Morning, lovebug." Her hips shifted back to make room as both boys climbed up on stools and reached for their toothbrushes. Especially this morning, she would have appreciated an ounce of privacy, but the assembly line was already being organized. They brushed and spit in a harmonious trio, followed by three face-washes, and then immediately the boys scrambled up on the vanity and perched on either side of her. Aaron patiently held the hairbrush and Parker automatically started to open lipstick tubes to figure out which one matched her outfit. Some day that decision could take time, but today her outfit for work was jeans and a fisherman's sweater. Parker could choose any color he liked, his favorite game.

"Which perfume today, Zoe?" Aaron asked sleepily.

"This one. You can spray it." Neither showed the least expression when she unlocked the medicine cabinet to remove a vial of perfume, though they both knew darn well she usually kept the scents on the dresser in her bedroom. "Did you give Uncle Rafe a hard time yesterday?" she asked casually.

Two small jaws dropped. " 'Course not. We were wonderful," Parker assured her.

"I take the question back," Zoe said wryly. "Let's put it this way. You are going to go *easy* on Uncle Rafe today, understand?"

"Sure."

"Sure."

"Because if you go *very* easy on Uncle Rafe today, late this afternoon you can come visit me and my whales."

"We will be *awesome*."

She listened patiently to the rash promises. Aaron was going to make lunch for everyone. Parker was going to remember to flush every time. Both planned to cultivate silence. No one was going to hit anyone even if Aaron hit him first.

" 'Scara, Zoe?"

"Thank you." With the mascara wand in her hand, she leaned closer to the mirror, her movement mimicked by the two urchins, who never seemed to lose their fascination with the mascara wand. She'd just finished one eye when a fourth reflection appeared in the mirror.

All she could think of was: *and now we pay the piper.*

The man standing behind her was wearing navy-blue pajama bottoms, which were tied with a drawstring below his navel. His arms were loosely folded over a golden chest peppered with dark hair. His whiskered chin gave him an unkempt, dangerous look; his muscled shoulders again made Zoe think of a lumberjack's, and there was an elemental maleness about this particular man-fresh-out-of-bed that set her nerve endings rippling like the stir of a breeze on the surface of a cool, smooth pond.

His slash of a smile set off waves of more intimate proportions. Suddenly and privately conscious of a delicate tenderness between her legs directly related to the man in question, Zoe felt color seep up her cheeks. It deepened when he uncrossed his arms and moved directly behind her.

"You helping Zoe get dressed?" he asked the twins.

"We always help her," Aaron affirmed. "She couldn't do it without us."

"And I can see you do a terrific job." Yawning, he reached for his toothbrush...by sliding both arms under Zoe's from behind her, and made the boys giggle when he applied toothpaste to the brush the same way.

"You look like you got four arms, Snookums!"

And one set was distinctly male, not to mention what was pressing intimately against her back. She scolded him with her eyes in the mirror.

"Shouldn't I be brushing my teeth in front of the kids?"

Such innocence, and she must have jumped sky high when the fingers of his left hand walked all the way down her spine and ended up with a private little pat. "We'll just go out and start breakfast," she said swiftly.

He behaved no better in the kitchen. When she leaned over the table to pour corn flakes, her fanny was treated to a surreptitious squeeze. When she reached into the refrigerator for milk, Rafe reached in front of her, slid his hand over her breast, and emerged with butter for toast. At the sink, he stood behind her length to length. At the table, he brushed imaginary toast crumbs from her lips. When she bent down for good-bye kisses at the door, Rafe was third in line. He managed a loud smack like the kids, but those weren't a child's eyes staring back at her. They were a man's, and that unrepentant grin made sure she knew it.

She reached for the doorknob with a heart gone thumping and her nerves in shreds.

"Forgot your jacket, Zoe," he said idly.

"Yes." She rushed back to the front closet for her navy parka.

"Forgot your purse, Zoe."

The shoulder strap was dangling from his finger. Completely addled, she snatched that, too.

"Zoe?"

She turned back one last, exasperated time.

"Just wanted to make sure you hadn't forgotten anything else," he said cheerfully from the door.

Over lunch with her co-workers, Zoe considered sending Rafe a package of darts in payment for his dangerous sense of humor. She knew exactly what he didn't want her to forget. The foolish man—if she were knocked out, half dead, unconscious, or suffering from amnesia, she still couldn't forget having made love with him the night before.

But she wasn't about to pretend that making love solved their problems. She knew it simply aggravated them. For the long term, the twins had to come first. Slowly, her feelings about children had been changing over the last four weeks. Long-closed emotional doors were creaking open, sometimes painfully. Possibilities skimmed the corners of her mind, but nothing she was absolutely sure of yet, any more than she was sure of Rafe. No matter how often she'd seen him bestowing love and caring on the kids, he'd never once mentioned his willingness to take them on without her. All she knew—all she could know—was that making the best long-term decisions for the children had to be her first priority.

But those decisions didn't have to be handled quite yet, and it was short-term options that plagued her as she slid on a wet suit later in the afternoon. Rafe wasn't going to be content with making love one time, she knew that.

And she didn't want him to. Before Rafe, she'd never had to face how seriously both the surgery and Steven's rejection had affected her confidence as a woman. Because of Rafe, she was coming out of limbo. Feeling again, hurting again, living again, wanting again.

Zoe, you're in such trouble . . .

"She's in the third holding tank. Come on, I'll show you." Sandy bobbed a grin at the two boys and threw a quick appreciative glance at Rafe before pushing open the lab door.

Rafe bundled the twins into their jackets, which he'd unzipped during the makeshift tour of the lab and institute Sandy had insisted on giving them.

"Where is she?" Parker tugged at his arm.

Which was the problem that was twisting his gut. According to the little brunette, Zoe was in the water. With a blasted whale. Evidently, she spent a great deal of her time in the water with whales.

Teeth clenched and adrenaline pumping through his bloodstream, he leaned against the metal fence with the kids and waited. When a sleek white fin emerged on top of the water, he felt his stomach tighten up in an acid ball. When the whale arched in the water and lunged back down, he caught a glimpse of the mammal's size and came darn close to losing his lunch. Zoe was *in* there? Sure, she'd told him what she did for a living, but if he'd really had any idea . . .

"Well, hi! Darn it, I expected to be done by the time you guys got here!"

"Zoe!"

"Snookums!"

Both boys rushed over to the ladder. Rafe had to wait a minute before the bile trickled back down to his stomach. In a sleek black wet suit, she looked even more petite and far more vulnerable than usual. Halfway up the ladder, she tugged off the hood and tossed her hair. Her smile was natural and infectious, her eyes sparkling with life.

"Well? Did you see George?" she asked the little ones.

"Is *that* George?" Aaron motioned to the water.

"That's George . . . probably the biggest baby in the entire Pacific. Not that he's so large for an orca, he isn't; he just seems to require more pampering than your average ten whales put together."

"Did you pet him, Zoe?"

"I'll tell you exactly what I did with him in just a second." After peeling off her scuba gear, she tugged off her flippers and then started to unzip her wet suit, talking all the while.

She told the kids how whales had a fantastic gift called echolocation. "See, toothed whales, like the orca, can send out sound beams so powerful that they can detect the presence of their prey, or their enemies, and they can use those same sound beams to find their way if the water's dark or murky." She told them that when something went wrong with a whale's echolocation powers, it could become disoriented and confused; it could even swim toward shore and get stranded at low tide. She told them about the experiment she was doing with George, and a two-ton magnet in the water. "See, the deal is this, guys. Scientists figured out that those sound beams are affected by magnetism. You know what a magnet is, don't you? And whales are incredibly smart, but not smart enough to understand that certain parts of the land are loaded with magnetism—just as if they were zillions of little magnets in the ground. And we don't want those whales to get stranded, so we figured . . ."

The kids asked questions almost faster than she could answer them. Rafe listened, and loved her. Her hair dried fast in the brisk breeze, and locks of chestnut silk fluttered around her face. Her skin turned pink from cold, and she shivered when she first climbed out of the wet suit and tugged on a navy sweat shirt that was obviously three sizes too large for her. Her slim hands moved expressively when she talked; he loved those hands.

Memories of last night washed over him like a fog. He couldn't let her go. She was a blend of fragility and incredible courage, all give and subtle stubbornness. Animated like this, she gave the impression that she thrived on blithe laughter. He'd never met a more complex woman, or one so deeply caring at the core.

"You *sure* that doesn't hurt George?"

Zoe leaned over to ruffle Aaron's hair. "Of course I'm sure, lovebug. I'd never do anything to hurt George. In fact, he's perfectly free to go whenever he wants, but he's sort of adopted us here. See, he lost his mom, and we fed him from the time he was a baby, so I think he's got this idea he's half human—"

"You have some kind of weapon when you're down in the water?"

"Weapon?" She raised surprised green eyes to Rafe's. At that exact instant, he felt something tight begin to ease inside him. She just looked at him, but it was the way coral suddenly touched her cheeks, the way her lips parted, and the sparkle in her eyes turned helplessly soft. All day long, he'd been afraid she'd do something damn foolish, like think too analytically about what had happened the night before. All day long, he'd been braced for the argument that last night had been a one-time-only occurrence for her.

He knew she wasn't ready to talk about a lifetime commitment; he knew she didn't yet believe such a commitment was possible for her, not in any relationship where children were involved. Truthfully, he was so certain he'd have a fight on his hands when he saw her today that her soft smile took him aback. Maybe that enigmatic curve of her lips disturbed him even more than a fight would have.

"A weapon, Zoe. Do you go down there protected, in case something goes wrong?"

She shook her head. "Of course not."

"You usually go down with another diver, at least?"

"Often, yes, but not always. There's a monitor in the lab, and no one's ever down for long without someone checking, so occasionally we dive alone. Some whales, particularly the orcas, develop confidence in only one person." She cocked her head, as if trying to fathom the reason for his questions. "Rafe, even a toothed whale wouldn't hurt a human unless it was threatened or hungry. Believe me, I know what I'm doing."

"Exactly how much does George weigh?"

"I don't know. somewhere around three tons, I imag—"

"Get dressed, would you? You and I are going to have a little talk."

He delivered his little talk on the beach after dinner, to Zoe's amusement. He phrased his questions very carefully, so he wouldn't come across as a Neanderthal-macho-chauvinist. "Look, you could rent out boats if you like the water so much. Or teach oceanography. Or run an aquarium . . ."

The boys had raced ahead and were playing catch with the tide. The wind had calmed down like a dream, and the water had the sheen of a green pearl blanket. Waves lapped softly, with a rhythm like music and a salt-sting freshness that she inhaled greedily and that was heady as champagne. She tucked her arm in Rafe's to comfort him because he was so distraught. "Have I said one word about your work with earthquakes?

You're going to tell me that doesn't have an element of danger in it?"

"That's completely different."

"Certainly it is. Because you're a male, you ox."

He gave a frustrated sigh. "This has nothing to do with my being a man. It has to do with you being damn fool enough to play with three-ton breaching 'babies.'"

"Earthquakes are harmless, hmmm?"

"I study them. I don't make a point of being there when one hits."

"I study whales. And I'm really outstanding at avoiding those that aren't too fond of humans."

"You're only a hundred and ten pounds!" Rafe roared.

"So *that's* it." She nodded sagely. "I can't tell you how easily that problem's solved. All we have to do is buy doughnuts on the way home. Believe me, I could gain another two pounds really fast."

He knew better than to push Zoe, but damn the woman! It wasn't his fault; she gave him no immediate choice. He swung her around and laced his arms around her neck and clamped down on her lips fast and hard. he wanted her *safe*. Preferably naked, warm, beneath him safe, and then if she was still in a sassy mood, he'd welcome that, too.

His hands wandered through her hair. The silky strands were all wind-rumpled; her cheeks had the slightest coat of salt, and her lips tasted sweet, far too sweet. Her tongue flicked between them, and he thought with despair, *More sass. Now how am I supposed to stay mad at you, Zoe . . .*

Her arms curled around his neck, and he knew the exact moment she went up on tiptoe; her slim thighs

pressed against his for balance at the exact same time
the blood surged through his veins like whitewater
rapids. The slight but deliberate rotation of her pelvis
against him was unmistakable. Her hand climbed back
down from his neck, and her fingertips drew lines down
his spine, little teasing lines that ended brazenly on his
rear end. The little witch was pressing. There wasn't a
chance in hell he could be seen in public for the next
twenty minutes.

He broke off the kiss only because there was a
damn good chance she was going to be naked in three
seconds flat in front of all Puget Sound if he didn't.
He glanced up swiftly, but the kids were now a good
distance from the water, climbing and sliding down a
miniature sand dune. Still, kids and water were
always a potentially dangerous combination, and he
forced his pulse to climb down from the sky. His eyes
flickered back to Zoe. "You realize what's going to
happen to you when they're asleep, don't you?"

"I have a fairly good idea."

"You don't have *any* idea," he corrected gruffly.

She nodded agreeably, but her eyes were dancing.
"I guess I don't have any idea."

"Your jeans—I'm going to have a particularly
good time peeling off those jeans of yours."

"Yes."

"And I'm going to kiss you. Starting with your
toes. Working up to the backs of your knees. I'm
gong to kiss your thighs. And you know what I'm
going to do to you then?" He brushed a strand of hair
from her cheek possessively. He suddenly understood
her fascination with the sea. Her eyes were like the
sea, fathomless, silver-green, lonely sometimes,

dancing with exhilaration sometimes, secretive sometimes. Her eyes were secretive now, filled with a woman's secrets, elusive, compelling, disturbing. "Why aren't you fighting me?" he whispered.

"Would it do any good?"

"None at all."

The wisp of a smile didn't quite reach her eyes. "I came to that same conclusion. Would you like to hear me say that I want you, Rafe? Because I do. And that I love you? Because I think I fell just a little bit in love with you as far back as a wedding six years ago."

Her words might have satisfied him yesterday. "I want you to see that there's nothing we can't work out. But that solutions that start with two are best. With you and me. With being honest about what we have."

She said nothing, just offered him a smile.

"Zoe?"

The children bounded up, and there wasn't a prayer on earth he could get his answer after that.

She gave him back rubs most evenings. He needed them. One night he made brownies—he claimed it was his one baking specialty and it was, but she'd never seen a kitchen so completely destroyed at the end of the little project.

"I'll clean it up," he promised. "You weren't supposed to come in here until I was finished."

"What did you do, mix them on the floor?" She grabbed the dishcloth and started filling the sink with sudsy water.

He got out a sponge mop and attacked the chocolate-spattered floor. "No criticism of the cook allowed until his product's been tasted."

"I can't taste them," she said swiftly. "I'm sure they're terrific, Rafe, but I can't."

"Why?"

"Because I have this thing about brownies."

"I know that. You crazy woman, why on earth do you think I made them?"

She shook her head firmly. "If I could stop at one —but the thing is, I've never had the strength of will to stop at one. And they go straight here, Rafe." She clapped her hands ruefully on her hips.

His frown looked dead serious as he rinsed out the mop and put it away. "Where do they go?"

"To my—"

"Show me exactly."

"Behave," she said in the ominous tone of a schoolmarm.

"You've got room for one brownie here. And another one here. And if we unbutton your jeans—"

"We?"

He popped a chunk of brownie between her lips. "Besides, I know an excellent way to work off calories. Chew fast, sweet. You're going to like this exercise program."

Zoe toyed with a pencil and stared unseeing at the stack of papers on her lap. Feet propped on the desk, she had a report to do that was going to be finished by lunch if it killed her. A staff meeting was scheduled for one; she had to concentrate.

Only she couldn't think. They were nearing the end of the second week in Washington. At the end of three weeks, Rafe's leave would be over and he would have to return to Montana. They had to decide what to do about the children.

They had to decide what to do about the two of them as well.

For two weeks, they'd tucked the kids into bed and then played. For two weeks, Zoe had had a lover of a kind she could never possibly find again. For two weeks, she'd slept, breathed, imbibed being in love with him. For two weeks, she'd been able to feel herself growing stronger and stronger as a woman, and that was the exact draw of Rafe, the exact reason why she'd never been able to say no to him.

She was a passionate lady with a right to express her feelings. She had a right to feel good about herself. To feel whole. To feel wanted for herself. Rafe had ingrained all of those feelings in her until a new Zoe had taken shape, a woman who was not afraid of children, a woman who was not afraid she was less than adequate, a woman who finally felt ready to let good healthy scars heal over the old wounds, and go on.

She'd fallen in love with a man and two children over the weeks they'd been together. The pencil broke in her hands, and she stared at it, distressed. She'd been living with a rash of secret maybes for days. Maybe the four of them could make it work. Maybe she no longer needed a contract signed in blood. Maybe Rafe's feelings for her had nothing to do with wanting a caretaker for the kids.

Unfortunately, she was less and less sure of his feelings for the boys. She knew—dammit, she *knew* he loved them. He wasn't a selfish man, but he kept making little comments to the effect that she shouldn't jump to the conclusion that he was ready to handle them. He claimed he couldn't. He claimed he wanted a lifestyle built around two, not four.

She'd kept thinking time would change his mind. Six weeks might not be enough time, but it was all they had. The situation was complicated by their work, which forced them to live in different states. How would they solve that problem?

But there was no solution at all if Rafe really didn't want the kids. She couldn't desert them. Her doubts about being a good mother were still strong, but not like before. How could she possibly choose between the only man who'd ever really mattered to her and the children, who had no one but Rafe and her?

Guilt racked her like pain. She was the one who'd put them all in a position of emotional risk. If she'd been less selfish, none of this would have happened. If Rafe had been less than Rafe, if she'd needed him less, if she could have loved him less, if she'd never let that first kiss happen, if she'd never . . . a thousand guilts pounded in her head. She couldn't seem to live with any of them.

A phone jangled in the next office, and she'd swung her feet off the desk before she heard Sandy's bright voice answering it.

"Zoe?"

Dragging a hand through her hair, she picked up her receiver.

"Zoe. Parker's sick. Come home, would you?"

She was home within twenty minutes. As she

burst through the door, she wasn't absolutely sure who looked sicker, Parker or Rafe. Wrapped in Rafe's arms, the little boy clutching his blanket; his eyes were teary and his complexion so white her heart turned over. But Rafe—until now she'd never seen him less than cool in an emotional crisis. His face was drained to ash color; his eyes were frantic, and his hair looked as though he'd run his hands through it a thousand times. As he paced the room with Parker, Aaron trailed after the two of them like a forlorn waif.

"He was fine this morning," she said swiftly.

"His fever's a hundred and one! He was perfectly okay, and then all of a sudden—"

"I'll call a doctor."

"We're not *calling* a doctor. We're *going* to a doctor."

"Yes."

"Or a hospital. Dammit, where's the closest hospital?"

In every problem with the kids, she'd been the one to panic and he'd been the rock. For that reason alone, she strove for patience as Rafe strode through a crowded doctor's office and tried to bully the nurse into scheduling Parker as an emergency. Not that a far too warm Parker wasn't downright miserable, but there was a child with a broken leg and another little one with a cut on her arm that obviously needed stitching.

And Dr. Thornby's examining room barely held two, much less four. Zoe took the only chair, with Aaron on her lap. Rafe stood beside her, his hands crammed in his pockets, while the young doctor bent over an irritable Parker. Rafe had taken one look at Thornby and decided he didn't like the town's only pediatrician.

"He's too damn young," Rafe mouthed to Zoe.

"For heaven's sake, would you give him a chance?" she mouthed back.

"If you put that stick in my mouth, I'm going to throw up all over you," Parker warned the doctor. "I hate doctors, and so does my brother."

"See, the kids don't even like him," Rafe mouthed to Zoe. "I think he's a quack."

"Rafe." This time Zoe spoke aloud. She stood up, still holding Aaron, and handed him to Rafe. *"Sit,"* she ordered him firmly, received a look of shocked surprise, and wandered over to Parker.

"Listen, lovebug," she told the boy, "I know you don't feel good, but in this family we don't talk about hating anyone. Ever. If we're scared, we say we're scared. Okay, monkey?"

The doctor shot her a wink. "Believe me, I've been through this before. Not to worry." A few minutes later, he adjusted his stethoscope around his neck and said quietly to Zoe, "He has a little cold and a very mild ear infection—"

"Mild!" Rafe snorted from the corner.

"—which I can treat with an antibiotic. It'll clear up in a few days. I'll give you a prescription for a nonaspirin fever reducer, too. Bring Parker back in a week for a checkup. He should be perfectly healthy by then. In fact, it's my best guess he'll be stomping around in three days." He leaned over to pat Parker's knee and then smiled at Zoe. "For the father, I pre-scribe two straight shots before dinner and an early bedtime." He shook his head in disbelief. "Hasn't he ever seen the child with a little cold before?"

Parker peered around the adult bodies to level fever-glazed eyes on his brother. "Did you hear that? Uncle Rafe has to have the shots."

It was an hour before they were back home, because they had to stop at a drugstore for the prescriptions. By then, Zoe had high hopes Rafe would turn back into Rafe. Instead, she was ready to ship him off to the nearest asylum by the kids' bedtime. She was as concerned as he was, but pacing around the house like a caged tiger was *not* helping. And trying to reason with a four-year-old about why he had to swallow terrible-tasting medicine was all very nice, but it went on for thirty minutes until Zoe tipped the tablespoon in Parker's mouth and held his lips closed until he swallowed.

"*That,*" Rafe said heavily, "was cruel."

Zoe set a shot glass in front of him and went into the other room to get the kids into their pajamas. Aaron closed his eyes the minute his head hit the pillow, but Parker wasn't about to sleep. "My ear hurts, and I can't breathe when I lie down," he complained.

"We'll fix it so you don't have to lie down," she whispered back. Bringing in the rocker from the living room, she swaddled Parker in a light blanket and rocked him. When his cheek cuddled sleepily on her shoulder, she closed her eyes and felt love ache through her like a surprise.

She'd known feelings were growing inside her for the twins, but not like this. For three years, every time she'd seen a child, she'd thought of the children she couldn't have. For three years, she'd held her chin high and told the whole damn world she didn't care. She cared. She'd always cared, but the wonder was holding and loving Parker and not having an ounce of emotional baggage intrude on that. Parker was himself, not the children she couldn't have, not other children, not the source of something that had cut up her life. He was just . . . Parker. A little boy who needed someone to love him.

A little boy she loved very much.

Barely a half-hour passed before Rafe appeared in the doorway. On stocking feet, he edged toward the bed. Aaron never moved when Rafe adjusted his blanket, or even when he sat down at the foot of the bed near the rocker.

"Is he asleep?" he whispered, nodding at Parker.

"Yes."

"What can I do?"

"Nothing, love." The endearment slipped out.

His voice was as heavy as lead. "Zoe, it's entirely my fault that he's sick." He leaned forward. In the darkness, his features were blurred and indistinct except for the dark orbs of his eyes. "I told you I took them to the park a few days ago. But I didn't tell you it started to rain."

"If you don't stop this," Zoe whispered patiently, "I'm going to call the doctor to get you a knock-out drug. Dammit, Rafe, can't you remember getting a few sore throats and colds as a kid? And I've heard Janet say that Parker was prone to minor ear infections. The doctor said it was common and nothing to worry about. Getting wet never hurt anybody."

He said nothing for a while, and then, "Do you want me to rock him?"

"I'm afraid to move him for fear he'll wake up again."

He nodded, then carefully eased himself down on the bed next to Aaron. Finally, he admitted in a whisper, "I can't stand it, you know. Never could."

"What?"

"Feeling helpless."

At eleven she tried putting Parker back to bed, but he immediately woke and started whimpering. Rafe insisted on taking his turn in the rocker, and it was Zoe's turn to lie down on the bed. Parker was asleep within seconds, and not long after that so was Rafe, his chin nestled on top of the child's head.

Zoe couldn't seem to move away from her three males, any more than she could go to sleep. She studied Rafe's moonlit profile, loving him—maybe more so after today. Even a rock had the right to crumble sometimes. If she'd ever wondered what his Achilles' heel was, she certainly knew now.

Rafe had no tolerance for feeling helpless, for not being able to help those he cared about. It seemed to Zoe the most endearing and human of weaknesses, but it disturbed her as well. It was the first clue she'd had as to why he didn't want the responsibility of raising the children. Being a parent meant having to watch little ones stumble and fall, make mistakes and learn from them, suffer growing pains and colds.

Maybe day-in, day-out caretaking had taken its toll on Rafe. Instead of bringing him closer to the boys, perhaps the constant contact had sealed his feelings in the other direction. He had a fascinating job, an independent lifestyle that included travel and freedom. He valued privacy. Now, instead of enjoying stolen moments of lovemaking, he was faced with the prospect of wiping an urchin's runny nose all night . . . How could she blame him for not wanting to make that kind of change in his life?

Parker woke three times in the night. She and Rafe took turns rocking him. In the morning, his fever was down; he ate two bowls of cornflakes and picked three fights with his brother. Rafe kept studying him in disbelief. Finally, he poured coffee and shook his head as he whispered to Zoe, "I don't care *what* he looks like. I never want to go through another night like that one!"

She took a sip of the steaming brew, but it settled in her stomach like despair.

CHAPTER NINE

"Aaron? Parker? Rafe?"

The apartment might as well have been a tomb. Parker was long past well and deserved a treat. Zoe had left the institute early, hoping to talk the group into an early Friday night movie and dinner. Only there was no group.

Poking her head into the kitchen, she noted gleaming counters and clean dishes. Such perfection might have aroused shock and even alarm if she hadn't heard a muffled thump from the bedroom. Someone was alive and well. Unbuttoning her jacket, she traveled the hallway to her bedroom door, where she took a long, amazed breath.

Two suitcases were propped on her bed. Neither of them was hers, although one was rapidly being filled with her clothes. Rafe was frowning in total masculine puzzlement over the difficulties of neatly folding a pink silk half-slip. Giving up, he tossed it on top, where it promptly slithered into a reasonably neat little heap.

The suitcases more than earned her surprise, but Rafe was the shocker. Used to seeing him in jeans and sweat shirts, Zoe noted the sharply creased tan cords, the calfskin vest, the gleam of a gold watch she hadn't seen before. His chin was so smooth that his shave couldn't have been an hour old, and a whiff of English Leather drifted toward her nostrils, distinctly and traditionally masculine. She had reason to know he was a handsome man, even when he was fresh out of bed, but spiffed up, he was darn close to kill-for material.

She delicately cleared her throat, which earned her a fast swivel of a man's head and blue eyes that reflected dismay, surprise, and, if she wasn't mistaken, guilt.

"You seem to have misplaced two children," she mentioned.

"You're home early!" He glanced swiftly back to the suitcases. "I can explain . . ."

"Good, because for a minute I thought I'd had wine for lunch. I never have wine for lunch, but for some reason those look like my clothes being packed."

"Yes." A wisp of a masculine grin. "Now, let's not panic, Zoe. This is a good surprise, not a bad one—although I admit I'd have been a lot happier if you hadn't shown up until five. There's one awkward detail . . ."

"Just one?"

"Yes, but it's a big one. Remember, Zoe, I've only got one week left of my leave of absence. So next week we have to sit down quietly and discuss what we've both been avoiding talking about: what to do with our urchins."

Her heart promptly pitter-pattered in both hope and despair. From Rafe's expression, she couldn't tell which emotion was more appropriate. If she hadn't brought up the subject, it was only because she couldn't face listening to what she didn't want to hear. If an ending was coming, she wanted to postpone it as long as possible.

"But not this weekend, Zoe. This weekend I specifically *don't* want to talk about children. I think it'll do us both good to get away from them for two days. I want you alone. I *need* you alone." He glanced up from the shirt he was folding and went totally still. His gaze intimately searched her face. "And I counted on you wanting to come with me," he said quietly.

She couldn't seem to stop looking at him. "Yes." The word was soft and simple. For a moment, the word seemed the only thing that mattered, but of course it wasn't. "But—"

"But," he echoed, as he turned back to his packing, "I had to find a sitter for the kids if we were going to escape for two days. Good sitters aren't exactly flying around free. I had to find someone who could handle scoundrel-age boys. Someone you would trust implicitly. Someone I woulwould take to like weeds take to water."

The strangest expression crossed his face. He cleared his throat, and his voice had a sudden boyish gruffness."Look, Zoe. Choices weren't exactly popping out of the woodwork. If I wanted to be alone with you, I had to find an answer. It was that simple. I don't want you to be embarrassed, but when push came down to shove, there was really only one person I could ask."

"For heaven's sake, would you just tell me who you're talking about?"

"His mother." Tall and lanky, with a no-nonsense hairstyle and a smile that radiated warmth, Marjorie Kirkland stood in the doorway for only seconds before swiftly moving forward. "And you have to be Zoe. My son appears to be thoroughly embarrassed that there could be an occasion in a grown man's life when a mother would still come in handy. I hope to heaven *you're* not. I'm absolutely delighted to be here. The boys and I have been getting on like a house afire."

The drone of the Piper's engines blocked out any potential for conversation. Beyond his seat, her seat, and two suitcases, there was barely enough room for the controls in front of Rafe. It was nearly sunset when they flew over the Columbia River, which marked the boundary between Washington and Oregon.

Zoe, silent, cocked her head toward Rafe bemusedly. She knew they were headed toward southern Oregon, but she hadn't the faintest idea how he'd managed to rent a plane . . . or that he had two brothers, a fact she'd learned from his mother, or that he knew how to fly. The questions would wait. At the moment, she was busy absorbing the knowledge that she had Rafe to herself for two whole days. Her heart sang the bittersweet refrain that these two days might be all she'd ever have.

An hour with his mother had been enough to convince Zoe that Marjorie was an angel, and an angel who was more than familiar with little boys. She had a gift for making people comfortable. Initially, the situation had struck Zoe as impossibly awkward. What could Marge possibly think of a woman who would casually take off for a fun-filled weekend, leaving two kids in her wake?

Only Marge, as it happened, was an enthusiastic proponent of fun-filled weekends. She had two other sons who regularly called her to baby-sit so they could enjoy weekends of a similar nature with their wives. Marge figured such things saved marriages. In the case of her one bachelor son, she hoped it would make a marriage. "Rafe gave me a very serious song and dance about how you two needed some private time to discuss the children," Marge told her frankly. "I admire both of you for taking on Aaron and Parker, but I knew the minute I saw my son's face that kids were the last thing on his mind. I've never heard so much throat-clearing in my entire life. Good heavens, you'd think by now he'd realize I know a little about life."

Marjorie Kirkland was a blend of frankness and subtlety, humor and common sense. She also knew the difference in He-Man figures between Skeletor and Moss Man, and the boys had been so absorbed in playing with her that a kiss and a quick squeeze at the door had been all they could spare for Zoe and Rafe.

"Cat got your tongue?"

She turned her head with a smile. "No."

Rafe glanced at a dial in front of him and then shot her an easy grin. "Well, it's got mine. I'm terrified I won't remember how to have an adult conversation. I don't think either of us has had the chance to finish a sentence in the last five weeks." He hesitated. "You're not worried about them?"

She shook her head. "Not at all."

"Good. Relax, Zoe. It's past time the two of us shared a very different world."

Like the slow seep of a sunset, Zoe felt that different world gradually take hold of her senses. The cool cockpit and steady engine drone ended in the total stillness and silence of a hideaway landing strip tucked in among mountains. A rental car was waiting for them. Rafe seemed totally familiar with where they were and where they were going, but Zoe had no idea and increasingly didn't want to know. Magic was stealing up on her like a secret.

Each minute took her farther from her work, the children, her apartment. The night was crisp, and midnight was creeping closer. Simple weariness slowed her blood to a languid pace, yet her heart kept beating with anticipation. She was alone with him. In all this time, she really hadn't been alone with him.

Especially during the last few days, the future had yawned ahead of her like a chasm without a bridge to span it. Even arranging this weekend struck Zoe as further proof that Rafe missed the privacy and freedom and choices that a life with children made impossible. Decisions waited like the dread of a toothache, yet perhaps that added to her growing excitement, desperation, recklessness. She had now. She had Rafe. There was a time when she hadn't believed in living for the moment, but this was different. If one only had minutes, the seconds were precious. These two days with him were hers —they had to be.

Neither lights nor road signs marked the gravel path where he finally turned in. Moments later, Zoe stepped out of the car, mesmerized. The thunder and roar of the sea were unmistakable. Jagged rock cliffs and the glistening sheen of moonlight. This place was a blend of her world and his, mountain and ocean, and nestled in a cradle of rock was a cabin, dark and wind-weathered, its windows overlooking the sea.

Rafe stood for a minute, watching her with a small smile on his lips. "Like it, Zoe?" he asked softly, but he knew. From the ease of her smile to the helpless gesture she made with her hands . . . she didn't have to say anything.

He carried the suitcases inside, and by the time she wandered through the door, he had a fire started in the corner hearth. Flames were already starting to lick the dry cedar logs. A kerosene lantern sat on the only table.

"Yours, Rafe?" she asked idly.

"It was. I sold it to a friend two years ago, but he rarely uses it except in the summer. He didn't mind lending it to us for a weekend."

She nodded, arms loosely folded around her chest as she explored. The cabin was as small as it was unexpectedly luxurious. Thick rust carpeting complemented the rich teak paneling. The double bed in one corner had a feather comforter and a mountain of down pillows. The kitchen ell was tiny, but stocked with everything from wok to microwave. Two oversized chairs flanked the fireplace, on both sides of a long couch in rust velvet.

A bath and a long storage room opened off from the main cabin. The bathroom ceiling was a skylight; the fixtures were brass and the towels pamper-thick.

Everywhere, she could hear the sea. Everywhere, she was conscious of isolation and privacy, of the romance implicit in the situation for two people who'd craved being alone for weeks, of Rafe watching her explore, waiting for her in total silence.

He still said nothing when she finally knelt beside him on the carpet by the hearth, but his gaze settled on her like an intimate touch. She suddenly registered the hammer-beating of her heart, her not-quite-dry palms, the texture of fragile feminine nerves. Her pulse throbbed with inordinate sensitivity; she wasn't sure what to say, what to do. She'd always been natural with Rafe—she'd never had any choice but to be natural with Rafe—but these circumstances were different. Before, she'd always known that two children could interrupt them at any minute. Her heightened awareness of Rafe was a measure of her knowledge that no one would interrupt them now, any more than anyone could save her from a man who suddenly seemed part stranger, vibrantly sexual, and inescapably male.

She didn't want to be saved. She just wished she could find something reasonably intelligent to say.

His jacket was gone, and so were his shoes. Clamped between his knees was a long green bottle, so recently uncorked that vapor still rose in wisps from its neck. He poured the sparkling wine into two stemmed glasses that gleamed like crystal in the firelight. The man's eyes had a far more purposeful gleam when he handed her a glass. "I figured it was about time I found out if you could handle your wine, Zoe."

"Yes?"

He nodded, his voice hushed and throaty. "Do you realize how much there is about you that I don't know? Simple things, like whether you get silly on champagne. What you look like all dressed up. What you'll look like when I wake you first thing in the morning. Or what colors you like—or what *you're* like, naked, when there isn't a soul around for ten miles and you know exactly what I want to do to you— Careful, sweet. You nearly spilled the wine."

She was so shaken she could barely manage the first

sip. "Rafe," she said slowly, "I think you're deliberately trying to unnerve me."

He gave her a lazy smile. "A little."

The champagne sizzled over her tongue, as heady as dancing blue eyes that spelled trouble as they peered over the rim of his glass. "It seems to me that a gentleman would make a little effort to make a lady feel at ease in a circumstance like this," she scolded him.

"But then, I'm not always a gentleman, and I hope to hell you're in no mood to be a lady. Have you had enough of that yet?"

"I just had one sip! And you just opened the bottle—" She snatched the glass away when he tried to take it from her. "Wait a minute, just wait a minute." She took a breath. "It's going to take me a second or two to put on a sophisticated face and pretend I know how to handle all this . . . attention."

He managed to remove the glass from her hand, pin her flat on the carpet, and still not make the first seductive move toward her. Balanced on his elbow so his weight wouldn't crush her, he gave her his gravest frown. "Sophisticated faces never cut much ice with me, and it's not attention you should be worried about handling. It's lust."

"Are you tactfully trying to warn me I've been kidnapped by a savage?" She reached her hand up to push aside the disobedient lock of hair that habitually strayed to his forehead.

"More or less."

"I'm shaking."

"No, you're not. You're relaxing. I'll even give you your wine back if you'll promise not to clutch the glass as though you're worried I've turned into a stranger."

"I don't need the wine, but, Rafe?"

"Hmm?"

She motioned generally to the room beyond him. "You planned. A lot," she accused quietly. "The plane, your mother, this place, the car. This is a lot more than a whim you thought up on the spur of the moment."

"Yes."

"I think . . ." She hesitated. "I think you should have asked me."

He nodded and set his glass on the hearth. "I know I should have asked you, but I wasn't willing to risk your saying no." She was wearing a coral blouse with a neckline that annoyingly blocked his view of her throat and that for some inconceivable reason buttoned at the shoulder. He opened those buttons one at a time. "You have extraordinary green eyes, love."

"You never told me you had two brothers. That you could fly. Where you rented the plane. How you found this place—"

"Suddenly, you're chattering like a magpie. Am I making you nervous again?"

"I want to hear more about your mother," she said stubbornly. "And what your father's like. I didn't even realize you came from South Dakota, did you know that?"

"You *are* nervous." His breath fanned her lips just before his mouth touched down. "Good," he murmured with satisfaction.

The Oregon sun filtered in the windows. The cabin was cool by morning, and invaded by the smells of sea and woodsmoke. Rafe watched her sleep, aware of the faint, lingering scent of her perfume. Her skin had the blush of dreams, and her hair was tousled on the pillow. Zoe inevitably slept sprawled on her tummy, except for those times he'd tucked her close to him in the night.

He'd kept her tucked close until dawn, and he had in mind keeping her close for a lifetime, but Zoe . . . he was so unsure of Zoe.

Especially these last two weeks, he'd carefully led her to believe that kids were a low priority for him, but it was like traveling on quicksand—he didn't know how to be careful enough. The kids had nothing to do with what he felt for Zoe, but getting her to believe that had him tied up in knots. That Steve character had wanted her on a package-with-children basis; there was no way he wanted her to think this was the same thing.

He'd deliberately told her he couldn't handle the responsibility of children alone. He'd deliberately tried to show her that he felt just as inadequate as a father as she could possibly feel as a mother—when Parker was ill, for instance. If she could just see that the little imps needed *both* of them, he knew they could work through any lingering fears or negative emotions she'd built up about children. She adored the twins, whether she knew it or not. And so did he, but it was a thousand times more important to make Zoe see that there was nothing they couldn't tackle as a twosome.

He didn't plan to spend the long stretch of lonely years without her, but two days wasn't long enough to make absolutely sure Zoe felt loved for Zoe. He had in mind binding ties and complicating her emotions and wearing down her resistance and stealing the alternatives away from her. He had in mind sneaking in some love whenever he could. He had in mind assaulting the lady where she was most vulnerable.

Sleeping, she was most vulnerable. Gently, silently, he slid the comforter off her, then the sheet. Her bare skin had the satin glow of sleep, and the long expanse from the nape of her neck to her toes confronted him with far too many options for the ruthless assault he had in mind. Her slim thighs were his personal preference, but he could also build a ladder of kisses up her spine. Her neck enticed him, but so did the curves of her calves.

It was going to be a long war if the choice of first battle was going to be this difficult. Finally, he chose her fanny, primarily because he was sure no one had ever begun a seduction with Zoe on that particular portion of her anatomy. He attacked with assorted kisses, some butterfly soft, some lingering. The firm skin sloped with delicate feminine perfection, which he always knew. His tongue scouted the hollow at the base of her spine, and then dawdled down to the tops of her thighs.

Ruthlessly, his lips coasted down the long expanse of her right leg, then up her left. Where he kissed, she was his. He didn't dare miss a spot—it was a superstition, like avoiding stepping on cracks in the sidewalk. Everything would be all right... everything had to be all right... if he labeled every inch of her skin Rafe Kirkland's, if he did it gently enough, softly enough, lovingly enough.

Somewhere en route, he forgot the war.

It was Zoe's fault. Her skin had this scent, all sleepy female, and the supple texture of her flesh yielded so readily to lips and fingertips. Kisses climbed up her sides to where her breasts were being cruelly crushed to the mattress. His tongue laved that plumpness. When he heard the hoarse little murmur that escaped her throat, he felt irritable. "Lie still," he murmured. "I want you to wake up nice and slow."

"It's far too late for that," she whispered, and twisted over in one lithe, feminine move that did nothing for his sanity. The rosy tips of her breasts were tilted up, as neglected as the firm white flesh around them. Her tummy . . . he hadn't even touched her tummy yet, and below she had a lush pyramid of soft curls that needed finger-combing, teasing, kisses, the caress of a tongue . . . she still wasn't used to that kind of caress. She took for granted that he wouldn't want to. The lady had no idea how much he wanted to.

"Rafe . . ."

The single word drew his attention to her mouth, the curve and swell of her lower lip, the more fragile heart shape of her upper one. She tasted sleepy, possibly the most intimate taste a man could steal. There was only one spot on her body softer than the inside of her cheek, but he settled there first.

His hunger grew, the more sweetness he found with his tongue. Breathing was becoming an effort, and the temperature in the cabin seemed to soar. He had every intention of making this last for a good hundred years, but she wasn't helping by responding like an abandoned, sultry, wanton, vibrantly sensual . . .

"Rafe?"

"Honey, I'm so busy. Could we talk later?" He had more work wiping off that perfectly wicked smile of hers.

"There seems to be something terribly wrong with me," she murmured.

"Take my word for it, love. There is *nothing* wrong with any part of you."

There was. Heat had replaced bones, and the surface of her skin was shimmering. She'd wakened to a man intimately, sneakily, lazily taking advantage of her, and she'd entered into that spirit of play. One look at his eyes and she knew he wasn't playing any longer. Suddenly, neither was she.

Everywhere she touched, she could feel need rippling through his skin. His lips craved contact. Hands kneaded and clutched and held, suddenly not so gentle. Outside, lonely waves crashed endlessly on rock, the silkiness of water eroding the hardest stone over thousands of years. Zoe urged the man inside her where she could hold him, the deeper Rafe, the vulnerable Rafe, the Rafe who shouted with his touch how much he wanted and needed her.

When he claimed, she became silk. Flesh grew slick as they discovered their own desperate rhythm. The roar of endless loneliness was just outside, but not here. Her legs clamped around him, she drew him down into yielding softness, caring, hope, woman, love.

In claiming her, he drove in his need to have, to hold, to protect and care for, to love.

You can't turn away from this, she told him with her lips.

See what we have, he whispered in his heart.

She fought the climax because it would have meant the end, and she had all of him for this moment. It didn't work; it couldn't. Waves of sharp, bright color rolled through her like the tide, powerful and inescapable and relentless. Her lips released a fragile cry, and then he folded her close and held her and held her . . .

And held her.

"I'm *not* climbing that, you overgrown bully."

"You're probably more fit than I am. Come on, Zoe, you're no sissy."

"I'm *swim*-fit. Not *climb*-fit." Southern Oregon fashion, the sand dune facing Zoe was at least 150 feet tall. Rafe was sitting at the top holding a can of beer, the lazy good-for-nothing. She'd made it halfway. Considering how little sleep he'd allowed her last night and this morning, she evaluated that distance as reasonable. The weather bureau had reported the temperature as a cool sixty, but where sun beat down on sand Zoe could have testified to at least a hundred.

"Lunch is waiting for you at the top," he called.

"Bring it *down*."

"Nope."

"When . . ." She dug up fistfuls of sand as she crawled toward him. *"When* I get up there, Kirkland, you're going to be such dead meat. You're going to be such cooked goose. You're going to be such fried fowl . . ."

When she reached the top, panting and sweating, Rafe was lying flat on the sand holding his stomach. He seemed to have a small problem with laughter. That laughter ended up in a howl when she bent down and gave him a definite shove.

How the mighty do fall, and a 180 pounds had so much momentum on the slippery sand. Moments later, she sat on the top of the dune with a beer can in her hand and waved down. "You can do it, Rafe! You're no sissy!" she called down encouragingly.

"Listen, you turkey. I've got sand in my mouth."

"No kidding?"

"Ah, Zoe. You're going to be so sorry. When I get my hands on you . . . when I get my hands on you . . ."

"Uh . . . Rafe? Have you looked around recently?"

"Yes." Rafe smiled. "I've never seen you look more lovely." He'd found the dress in the back of her closet and packed it, so he considered himself partially responsible for her looks right now. The skirt was a simple black crepe, and the top a turquoise satin that draped to the hollow of her breasts. The sleeves seemed made of yards of material that cinched at her wrists, and the effect was alluringly feminine. He hadn't yet figured out what she'd done to her eyes and hair. Something. Something that made her eyes look emerald green and her hair gleam with shafts of gold and silky softness.

Zoe let her eyes sweep over him as well. He'd brought his tux—she hadn't known he owned one—and since the man had done the packing, the tux had a predictable wrinkle or two. Never mind that; black made his shoulders look impossibly huge, and it was his pride that struck her.

She ate the last bite of her fillet, and then took a sip of wine. "Rafe . . ." she started again.

He shook his head. "I wanted to see you dressed up, and I wanted to dance with you. Come on, Zoe."

She placed her napkin on the table and stood up, letting him lead her to the crowded dance floor. With one hand at her waist, his other hand covered hers on his chest. He picked up the subtle rhythm of the song. Not once did he move to hold her closer, but deliberately he let thigh occasionally tease thigh, chest occasionally flirt with breast. His eyes never left hers. He told her she was lovely, priceless, precious, and, so simply, that he wanted to be with her. He told her that without saying a word.

Sometime . . . sometime . . . she was going to mention to him that the band was playing country rock. That everyone else in the place was wearing jeans. That the only person with a candle on the table was the one who'd brought it, and that was Rafe. Southern Oregon didn't exactly abound in elegant restaurants.

Since neither of them cared a hoot what anyone else was doing, it didn't particularly matter.

"I hate to tell you this, little one, but you're turning into a downright glutton for pleasure—and all those little hip actions aren't going to do you a bit of good."

"No?" Embers of a fire glowed in the corner, casting soft shadows in the pitch-black room. Swallowed in the depths of the featherbed, Zoe nudged her pelvis delicately against Rafe. "I'm not claiming to be an expert in this," she admitted, "but I could swear I sense a certain effect."

His lips touched her forehead. "I didn't say you weren't having any effect. I said it wasn't going to do you any good. It's three in the morning, and you need your sleep."

"I can sleep next year."

His whisper grazed her skin like wet velvet. "You're sore."

"No, I'm not."

"You are. In between climbing dunes and dinner, I think you might remember that we were doing other things."

"Believe me, I remember."

He clasped both her hands patiently in one of his. *"No.* When I touched you the last time, you were sensitive. Dammit, did you think I didn't notice? We are *not* making love again—*Zoe.* Those are your teeth in my shoulder."

"You like that."

"Is that supposed to be relevant to anything in particular? You know darn well I like everything you do."

"You like this, too—good heavens! You like it a lot."

"You're sore," he repeated in the tone of a drowning man.

"A little. Not *that* much."

"That much is my fault."

"I could have sworn I was there at the time."

"You were."

"Rafe, I have an itch—"

"You do *not* have an itch, not there, and I am not letting go of your hands."

"All right. I think it's time we got serious here. Fifty cents says I can make you let go."

"No."

"Five bucks says you'll be breathing hard inside of three minutes."

"No."

"A hundred—flat on the line, and believe me, you'll never get this offer again—says you'll be inside me on the short side of ten minutes."

"If and when I meet your mother, Zoe, I'm going to tell her just what kind of daughter she raised."

Conversation lagged. He'd just released her hands.

From the rear window of the rental car, Zoe took one last look at the cabin. She thought, *it's over,* and tested every corner of her mind for regrets. There had only been so much time, and maybe they should have spent it talking about each other. Maybe they should have spent it talking about the children.

Instead, all they'd done was . . . be together.

She had no regrets.

As for all the decisions waiting to be made, she knew exactly what she was going to do. Loving him had clarified the only choice she really had.

CHAPTER TEN

"MY GOODNESS, I didn't expect you two back for at least another hour. I just put the boys to bed." Marjorie Kirkland hugged Zoe as naturally as she hugged her son. "Did you have a good time?"

"Wonderful," Rafe affirmed. "More important, did you survive the boys?"

"No problem at all, but what about you two? Have you eaten dinner?"

"Yes, Mom. We stopped for a bite on our way home from the airport."

"Well, I'm certainly going to make you a pot of tea, and the boys and I made oatmeal cookies . . ."

Zoe felt Rafe slide the jacket off her shoulders and gently squeeze her neck from behind. "Rather have a brandy?" he murmured to her when his mother disappeared into the kitchen.

She shook her head. The flight had left her groggy after forty-eight hours of sleeplessness. The blaze of apartment lights and Marjorie's bright, curious eyes had struck her as a disorienting blur. She wanted to be able to think clearly, and instead couldn't think at all. "Nothing, thanks. But I think I'll check on the kids."

"Zoe?"

She turned back, but Rafe didn't say or do anything more than possessively brush a strand of hair from her cheek. Since their plane had landed, the silence between them had gradually become charged with a brooding uneasiness—her own doing, Zoe knew. Rafe had tried more than once to talk. Maybe if she'd let him, there would be less tension on his face now, less wariness in his eyes. She wanted to tell him he no longer had to worry about anything, but the right moment wasn't now.

Carrying her suitcase back to her bedroom, she dropped it just inside and noted that Marjorie's was neatly packed and ready for her departure in the morning. All she could think of was that Marjorie's son would also be leaving all too soon.

Switching off the light, she tiptoed toward the boys' room. The fuzzy darkness and silence enfolded her like a soothing balm as she moved closer to the bed. Both boys were asleep. Snuggled up to his blanket, Parker had kicked off the rest of his covers. She bent over to tuck him in again, dropped a soft kiss on his cheek, and then glanced at Aaron.

That fast, two arms reached up to her in the darkness. With a smile and a tug on her heart, she crossed to the other side of the double bed and leaned over to hug him.

"You're back," he whispered. "Is Uncle Rafe back, too?"

"Sure—he's in the kitchen right now. Did you have fun with Uncle Rafe's mom?"

"Yes. Snookums? Don't go."

She sank on the edge of the bed, smoothing his hair and the covers. "I'll stay for a minute, but you have to go to sleep, lovebug. It's late."

"I didn't think you were coming back."

Something welled in Zoe's throat. "Didn't you remember? I promised you we'd come home tonight."

"So did Mommy. But she didn't come back. Zoe?"

"What, darling?"

"Mommy's dead. She isn't coming back ever and my daddy isn't either."

He said it easily, bluntly, four-year-old style, as if he were informing her of something she might not have been sure of before. Zoe studied his eyes for tears, but she was the only one with sudden diamonds in her eyes. Propping her elbows on both sides of him, she leaned closer. "Know something?" she whispered lightly.

"What?"

"Part of your mommy and daddy can't ever die for you, did you know that? Any time you're feeling sad, all you have to do is close your eyes and feel how much they love you. Close your eyes and you can remember them kissing you good night; you can remember last Christmas; you can remember making cookies with your mommy and being snuggled on your daddy's lap. You're always going to be able to do that, sweetheart. Any time you want to, all you have to do is close your eyes to feel how much they love you. That love's still there, and it won't ever go away."

"Promise?"

"Cross my heart."

"Can we see your whales again tomorrow?"

Smiling, she tucked the covers around his neck and kissed him again. "We'll talk about it in the morning."

Slouched on the sofa with his long legs stretched out in front of him, Rafe had had his eyes peeled on the doorway since she'd left. When she finally wandered back in, he could see how tired she was. Pale mauve shadows made her eyes look huge, and her face was paler than cream. She needed sleep . . . but something more than fatigue had been eating at her all afternoon and evening.

He crooked his finger and motioned her next to him. She sank down on the couch's center cushion like a duchess, all straight spine and a proper distance away, not at all what he had in mind. He figured she was worried about propriety for his mother's sake.

He was worried about Zoe. He hadn't been able to make a dent in her long silence on the trip home—not that silence in itself had to be dangerous. No two people could have been any closer than they'd been over the weekend, and in his head he knew he'd gotten through to her. He'd felt her love, and heaven knew he felt oceans of love himself for her. As soon as his mother was gone, they could talk. Zoe was temporarily over-tired, but there was no reason to think anything was seriously wrong.

But there was. His pulse ticked an uneasy beat, af-firming it. Wrapping his fingers around her shoulders, he gently but persistently tugged until, like an accordion, she finally folded closer. Marge was talking thirteen to the dozen. His mother always talked thirteen to the dozen, and Zoe was starting to smile ... but it wasn't a Zoe smile.

Zoe smiles were spontaneous and mischievous and showed off perfect white teeth. When she really laughed, her eyes overflowed with joy. He tucked her into the curve of his shoulder, but her spine was still rigid, and the curve of her lips was distinctly polite. He told himself again that he could wait until his mother was gone in the morning. And knew, immediately, that he couldn't manage more than twenty more minutes before hauling her off to some private spot where he could find out what was wrong.

"... I should have brought pictures of when they were younger." Marge's knitting needles clicked as she rocked. "I've got tons of photographs, Zoe. Everyone's the same. Brian and Nathan stand there looking like angels, their hair all combed, their shirts tucked in ... and then there's Rafe. He always stood in the left side of the pictures; I don't know why. If he didn't have a black eye, he always had a scrape that showed. I swear I could have safety-pinned his shirts and they still wouldn't have stayed tucked in ..."

"Mom, Zoe is *bored*," Rafe said quellingly.

"She is not."

"I am not," Zoe affirmed.

The two women apparently enjoyed discussing embarrassing moments in his past history. Rafe might have been amused—his mother inevitably embellished the stories, and with such relish—if he hadn't seen what she was doing. His mom was a pro at sneakily maneuvering in exactly the direction she wanted it to go. That she'd taken to Zoe the instant she met her was obvious. That she was ignoring her son sent him the warning message that she was gearing up to delicately pry, a complication he definitely didn't need.

"Anyway, you're having your own experience raising boys, it would seem." Marge propped her glasses down on her nose to look over them at Zoe. Her steady stream of light conversation only gradually slowed to a gentler, more serious pace. "I think you two have done something perfectly wonderful, taking on those kids. Shouldering all the responsibility and juggling jobs and upsetting your lives—I don't think many people would have done it. But I have to admit I'm not very clear on your plans from here. Rafe mentioned he'd have to be back in Montana—"

"At the end of next week," Rafe finished for her, and droned warningly, "and I already told you we haven't made firm plans about the children yet."

"Did you, dear?"

"Yes. And I told you *why* we hadn't talked yet, which was that we agreed from the beginning to try *not* to form conclusions or make judgments until we'd spent as much time together with the kids as we could." Anyone who'd ever met Rafe could tell that the subject was now closed.

Marge chuckled sympathetically, looking directly at Zoe with an onward-and-upward determination that would have impressed a general. "Zoe, when Rafe leaves next week, are you staying here with the children? Or—"

"We haven't discussed that either, mom. But we'll work it out." For Rafe, the discussion of the subject was now ended.

"Of course you will, of course you will. It's all so complicated, with your jobs and all. I was just wondering . . ."

"Mother—"

Matched sets of blue eyes were snapping at each other. All Zoe could think of was that she wasn't ready —maybe she'd never be ready to face the impending talk with Rafe. But now was no worse than any other time, and she wouldn't have mother and son bickering when she could prevent it with a few words. "Naturally, you mother is curious about our plans," she scolded Rafe gently, and then directed a deliberate smile at his mother. "I'm taking the children, Marge."

It was an excellent argument-stopper. Rafe stiffened in total silence like a poker besider her. And Marge's lips stopped moving for the first time in half an hour; her knitting needles even stopped clicking. Zoe definitely had the floor.

Her palms dampened, and a huge ball of sadness swelled in her throat. Her voice stayed calm and quietly assured only because she demanded that of herself. "As Rafe said, we haven't work out all the details," she told Marjorie, and admitted frankly, "He's going to argue with me. You've got a wonderful son, Marge. I can't tell you how warm and loving he's been with the kids. He'd take on total responsibility for them in a minute, but I'm not about to let him do that."

"Dammit, Zoe—"

Gently, she raised her voice, her eyes focused only on his mother. "His work is important to him, and occasionally he's had to travel because of it, which would be almost impossible with two children. And in Montana, I can't imagine where he'd find day care. So much that he needs and wants in his life would be complicated by children. From the very beginning, I knew it was more logical for me to take them. My job hours are more flexible, and my work is more settled."

Marge stopped rocking altogether. "Yes, but my dear, I thought you two—I was so sure that—"

"Mom, you're tired," Rafe announced.

If mother and son occasionally bickered, it was rather obvious their wavelengths were also finely tuned to each other. "Good heavens, I certainly am." Marge shoved her yarn back into the knitting bag and stood up. "I'm absolutely exhausted. Can't imagine what I was thinking of, talking this late. It's after ten, and I've got a flight to catch in the morning. Now, you two just finish this nice pot of tea. Don't bother about me . . ."

A good fairy couldn't have disappeared faster, only Zoe touched her fingers wearily to her temples, not certain she wouldn't have been happier if the good fairy had stayed. Rafe had lurched to his feet and was standing with his hands on his hips, a glowering frown beamed directly at her. She saw a thousand things in his eyes. Frustration and love. Anxiety and irritation. Mostly she saw a man damn close to exploding, but his voice ladled out the surprise of gentleness. "Zoe, you're so tired you can't see straight. I'm going to get you a brandy. Just sit there, would you? Just stay right there."

She nodded, but the minute he was out of sight she dashed for the bathroom.

Hands trembling, she closed the bathroom door, turned on the light, and flicked on the cold water tap, so that the noise of the water would muffle the harsh low sound that escaped from her throat. Tears made rainbows in her eyes.

Crying was foolish. Her decision to take the children alone was best, and the only one she could make. She felt good about it. Wonderful. Ecstatic, in fact, and pressing a cool washcloth firmly to her eyes, she willed herself not to cry.

She was afraid he was going to argue, that he was going to try to talk her into a foursome. Being Rafe, he'd do that out of a sense of responsiblity. She couldn't let him do that. Over the long weeks, Rafe had given her an incomparable gift. Herself. She was Zoe again, the strong woman she'd forgotten how to believe in since her hysterectomy. She had only one gift to give him of equal measure—a sensitivity to his real feelings, as he'd been sensitive to hers.

In so many ways, he'd tried to tell her he didn't want the responsibility of children. She hadn't listened, but the weekend in Oregon had told her what he wanted and needed in his life: a woman who was free to dash off on a whim. The adventure of a one-on-one relationship with no strings attached. Freedom and privacy and spontaneity. He wanted a woman to climb mountains with; she'd always known it.

Rafe wanted her, she knew. And she also knew that he loved her, but in time he was bound to feel resentful if the lifestyle he really wanted wasn't possible. He'd find another woman, someone to whom he alone mattered, a relationship in which he wasn't roped down by years of sticky fingers and interrupted dinners and night-walking little ones with colds.

She was really very happy she'd come up with a solution that worked for all of them. Any minute now . . . any minute now . . . she was going to feel incredibly happy.

When the doorknob turned, she straightened instantly. Then, bending her head, she wrung out the washcloth. "I was just coming out," she said brightly.

Rafe came in and quietly closed the door behind him.

"Really. I was just coming back out . . ."

He reached around her to turn off the faucet. The silly thing was still running, and in the mirror her complexion looked somewhere past chalk and halfway to gray. Two strong hands cinched her waist, turned her around, and lifted her to the vanity. His fists came down like jail bars on either side of her. Her lungs suddenly had a hard time finding air, and she couldn't seem to look past the third button on his shirt.

"I *was*—"

"No, you weren't, Zoe. I don't know how long you were planning to hide out here, but my guess is two or three years."

She took a breath. "Your mother's still awake."

"My mother is entitled to stay up all night if she likes. She's a grown woman. She can make that kind of decision all by herself."

"She'll think there's something funny if we don't—"

"Probably. I really don't care. Put your arms around my neck, honey."

"That won't"— she took a huge breath—"change anything."

"Certainly it will. It'll make me feel a hell of a lot better." He raised one limp arm and curled it around his neck, then the other. One look at her face and a shudder had wrenched his heart. If the damn woman ever tried to hide tears from him again, she was going to get the worst scolding she'd ever heard in her life . . . or maybe not. He'd never managed to stay angry with Zoe for longer than two seconds at a time, and anger was distinctly the last emotion he felt for her now.

He nudged her forehead with his, well aware she was fiercely fighting to control her emotions. "One of us is slightly on the selfish side, Snookums." He meant to make his tone light and soothing, but somehow it escaped like the scrape of a tire on gravel.

"I know."

"No, you *don't* know, dammit. You think it's you."

"But it is, Rafe. I'm the selfish one." She tilted her face up. "I've spent six weeks thinking of me, of what I was afraid of, of what I could handle, of what I wanted and needed. You must have thought I never heard what you said about your own feelings. Liking kids isn't the same thing as wanting them. You've tried to tell me in a dozen ways that kids weren't important to you."

"I worked damned hard to give you that impression, but I never guessed it would backfire like this. I *want* the monsters, Zoe. Did you think I didn't?"

"You said—"

"That kids weren't important to me. That they'd never mattered. That I didn't want the responsibility of raising them. I know what I told you, and I admit that a few months ago I wasn't planning on listening to four-year-olds' monologues on a steady basis, but it's obvious that sort of thing grows on you. We're not just talking *growing;* we're talking clinging ivy. So we start adoption procedures tomorrow; all problems should be easy to solve." His matter-of-fact tone deteriorated into vibrating emotion. *"You're* the troublesome one, woman. Now, are you going to listen to me?"

"Rafe—"

"No talking. Just listen." She was such a mess. Where the washcloth had pushed up her hair, he pulled it back down again. For token color, he gently pinched her cheeks. And to erase the agony of uncertainty from her eyes, he lifted her chin so she could see the unquestionable sincerity in his.

"I *love* you," he said gruffly. "But if I'd let you think I could handle the kids, I was afraid you'd take a fast train in the wrong direction. I was afraid you'd think I wanted a package deal like that bastard who hurt you, and I was afraid you were overwhelmed by the responsibility of caring for our two miniature scoundrels, and I was afraid you'd feel pushed because we've had too damn little time alone together. Only I'd had enough time about ten minutes after I met you, Zoe, and living with a woman day and night for six weeks is a hell of a good way to get to know her. I've seen you mad, scared, sexy, irritable, joyful, serious, silly. I *love* you, and I'm talking long term. Permanent lease. Total dominion. So just say yes, and for godsake don't start thinking."

"Yes."

She wasn't sure he heard her. At some point during his ranting, his head had started coming down. His lips homed in on hers as her arms tightened around his neck. He molded an unfamiliar kiss on her lips. Her mouth was still sensitive from a long weekend of the taste and texture of Rafe; she thought she knew every variety of kiss in his more-than-versatile repertoire. Not this one.

This kiss was the fragile plea of a man who needed her to believe in him. His lips savored hers, holding on, afraid to let go. She tasted urgency and tenderness, beguilingly sweet need and the strong flavor of lonely desperation. *Love me,* said his kiss. *I need you, Zoe.*

She kissed back, so hard that tears stung her eyes. Believing in him was a choice she'd made a long time ago. Believing in herself had been the tough part, but she really couldn't doubt how he felt. Not now.

His lips trailed down along her jaw to her throat. "I love the lady who thinks she has no courage. The one who jumps in a tank with a three-ton whale. I love the lady with that tiny scar on her tummy." His lips pressed in her hair, on her temples. "I love Snookums. I love the woman who thinks she's so selfish. The one who crams two kids in a bathtub with her." His kisses coasted down her forehead, with one for the tip of her nose. "I love the Zoe who wears crazy hats, and the one who comes apart at the seams when she's touched in certain places. Can't you put me out of my misery, Zoe? Say yes."

"I already did, love," she whispered.

He raised his head. "Then say it again."

"Yes."

"And again."

"*Yes.*"

Slowly, he lifted her off the vanity and leaned back against the far wall, drawing her with him. Thigh pressed on thigh, heart beat on heart. The blue of his eyes made the sky look dull, and his smile possessively took in every inch of her face. "You don't get to take it back, you know."

"I don't want to take it back. Can't you understand how agonizing it would have been for me to let you walk out of my life? But I wanted what was right for you, Rafe. I didn't want you to have to sacrifice—"

"I can't seem to tell you enough that I'm the only selfish one in this twosome. I'm getting it all, sweet. Exactly what I want. Don't you dare still doubt it—or *ever* doubt that you matter more to me than life."

The moment's radiance softened. She touched his cheek. "I love you," she whispered. "I just wish I could have met you a thousand years ago. I wish I could give you children. I wish . . ."

"Ah, Zoe." He wrapped her up and buried his face in her hair in a hug so tight she could barely breathe. "I wish I could give *you* children, little one, only because I know how much that matters to you. I just hope that what I feel for you, what I want for you, will help to make that loss easier."

She held on, her eyes squeezed shut. Even if she'd just said it, she had to say it again. "I love you."

"Tell me again."

"I love you."

"Tell—"

"Lord, you're greedy." She lifted her head, and her eyes started to dance. "You meant it, about adopting Aaron and Parker?"

"Of course I meant it. Who else would be insane enough to take them on?" He said quietly, "I think it might help them to know we'll be there through thick and thin. And after that, we can adopt ten more if you want an even dozen. And after that we can change careers and run an orphanage or two."

"Thanks, but no."

He chuckled, but abruptly he grew serious. "We're *not* going to be separated, Zoe."

"No," she murmured.

"I *will* have to go back to Montana next week to clear things up, but I'll give them two weeks' notice."

"No, you won't," she said immediately. "I can give up my job just as easily."

"Don't tell me you're suddenly going to *seriously* turn selfish on me?" he scolded. "Look—I'm looking forward to being unemployed and supported by a woman for a while."

"And dogs have wings. You're just saying that so I won't have to give up my job, but you can forget it. Rafe, I love my whales, but the kids are already four. They're going to be in school soon enough as it is. For too long, I thought there'd be no children in my life. Now that I have the twins, I want to be home with them."

"Not forever?"

"No, not forever. But Alaska has both fault lines and whales, doesn't it? And so does California. And several universities sponsor projects in both our fields. We've got a little time before they're in school to look and plan."

His hands slid down her spine to her bottom. "We

could maybe worry about the details of all that to-morrow."

"We could." She leaned closer.

"We could even talk weddings if you want to."

"We could." She let her hands glide down his sides to his hips, and returned deliberately teasing pressure for deliberately teasing pressure. "We could also steam up the bathroom."

He cocked his head with the devil's own grin. "Every time I've seen that look in your eyes, it's meant bad news for my sanity."

"That's what I had in mind."

"We have two children and a mother in the house," he reminded her.

"Rafe," Zoe said firmly, "lock the door."

COMING NEXT MONTH

NO HOLDS BARRED #394 by Jackie Leigh
Eli Sutherland's content being an investment
manager by day and wrestler Stud Savage by night...
until Kate Harcourt begins playing Stud's "girlfriend" and
turns his carefully planned life topsy-turvy.

DEVIN'S PROMISE #395 by Kelly Adams
Twelve years after their shared youth, the roguish,
irrepressible Devin O'Neill is back for good—
and Cass Heath's determined not to lose her heart
again to this Irish charmer...

FOR LOVE OF CHRISTY #396 by Jasmine Craig
When policewoman Laura Forbes marries America's
sexiest heartthrob, TV superstar Bennett Logan, to help
him win custody of his daughter Christy, their
marriage of convenience proves to be anything but!

WHISTLING DIXIE #397 by Adrienne Edwards
Engaged in an amorous battle, snake curator
Roberta E. Lee's determined not to surrender—but
Yankee banker Stephen Grant's planning
strategies guaranteed to besiege her southern heart.

BEST INTENTIONS #398 by Sherryl Woods
Tough-talking Traci Marie has got things under control—
until her freewheeling ex-husband Doug Maguire comes back
to see his son, charming his way into her heart...

NIGHT MOVES #399 by Jean Kent
When Drug Enforcement Administration officer Greg
Heflin investigates Kelsey Sviderskas, he finds himself
falling for this trusting Swedish beauty—
or is he falling for a clever innocence act?

Be Sure to Read These New Releases!

FIRE UNDER HEAVEN #382 by Cinda Richards
Did Annemarie Worth and David Gannon fall in love during
the month of terror they endured together? She says no,
but he says yes...and he'll move heaven and earth to prove it!

LADY INCOGNITO #383 by Courtney Ryan
Who *is* the mystery woman who leaves Chad Delaney
holding her Las Vegas jackpot? Chad's search for
whimsical, vulnerable Alex Duffy leads to
a love-filled odyssey across the Arizona desert.

SOFTER THAN SPRINGTIME #384 by Frances West
Past betrayal formed Jo Rossi's bitter opinion of the
filthy rich. Now, forced to work with wealthy photographer
Michael Travis, she's afraid to trust his easy charm...and
unable to resist his captivating kisses...

A HINT OF SCANDEL #385 by Dana Daniels
When UFO investigator Darcey Dennison shows up on his
Missouri ranch, Trey Jones finds he's got a lot more
to worry about than an invasion of "little green men."
Suddenly the whole town's talking romance, and Darcey
seems destined to capture his heart.

CUPID'S VERDICT #386 by Jackie Leigh
When homespun farmer Jake Coltrane and wisecracking
Atlanta municipal judge Vivian Minnelli collide—
under *most* unusual circumstances—they emerge
fighting mad...and irresistibly, powerfully attracted!

CHANGE OF HEART #387 by Helen Carter
The depth and vibrancy of Alex Stratis' new play
strikes a chord deep within actress Marla Travis...
but Alex's own sensual chemistry offers soul-stirring
possibilities Marla's been afraid to face.

Order on opposite page

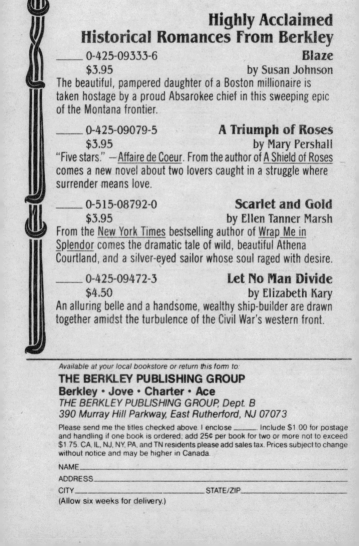